Preschool Prodigies
CHAPTER EIGHT
8

By: Robert and Samantha Young

Illustrations: Robert Young with art licensed at FreePik.com

Published by: Young Music, LLC
ISBN: 978-0999210161
Copyright © 2017
Preschool Prodigies and Young Music, LLC
2358 Dutch Neck Road
Smyrna, DE 19977

Prodigies Playground
THIS BOOK BELONGS TO:

_____

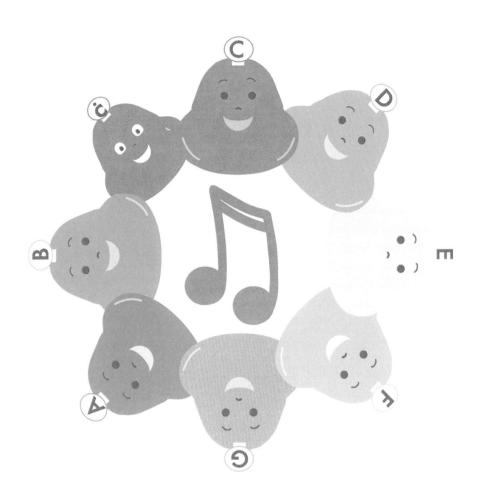

Dear families & teachers,

Welcome to the final Chapter of Preschool Prodigies. In this Chapter, we'll be working with all 8 of the C Major notes, as well as all of the hand-signs.

In Chapter 7, we focused a lot on chords. In Chapter 8, we'll focus more on melodies, popular songs and the Solfège hand-signs. It will be a bit easier than Chapter 7, which will let us end this semester nice and strong.

If you find that you have extra time toward the end of the year, it's worth revisiting the listening games from Chapter 7 (and other chapters). There are also Performance Tracks in the Playground that are great for putting on end-of-year shows.

If your kids aren't ready for a full-on recital, some call and response bell playing or hand-signing with you leading the way is still a huge crowd pleaser and a great way to make your Prodigies feel comfortable and confident at their first performance.

For my twos, threes and fours classes, some of our end-of-year shows were basically just the parents coming to music class. The process is important, and if you do have multiple students, letting their parents see a musical class will arm them with more activities to do at home.

Along the same lines, this book also contains a lot of posters, manipulative cut-outs and popular melodies that all make great send-home materials for continued musical play. With these materials, students can continue singing, signing, playing, sequencing and composing throughout the summer and come back next year ready to rock!

If you're thinking, **"What's after this book?"** consider the points below to determine your next steps.

1. For children 3-5, absolute pitch development takes 1-2 years of meaningful and regular exposure to pitch. This means some kind of musical or otherwise pitched practice 4-5x per week (at about 20-30 minutes per session). Don't forget that repetition is the key to mastery. Just watching the videos once is not enough. Practice makes Prodigies.

2. It takes about 3 months for children to feel confident with each chord. In other words, REPEAT THE CHORD LESSONS OFTEN! By month 3 (circa Chapter 3), children should feel confident with Do, Mi, Sol. Then through months 3-6, children should feel confident with Sol, Ti, Re. Then toward the end of their first year (circa Chapter 7), they should start to feel confident with Fa, La, Do. Use the listening games in each chapter to assess your students' pitch development. Then play your own listening games to keep it fresh.

3. Get creative with the manipulatives in these books. Cut them out, laminate them, and store them with your bells. Reprise the games we played in the Playground with just you and your kids. Work the bells into games like "Red Light, Green Light," or even work them into daily routines like an end-of-class melody or a dinner-bell melody. Also, look to the lesson guides in this book and the longer Lesson Plans in the Playground for ideas.

4. Go back to earlier chapters and play songs again. Again, practice makes Prodigies. Can your kids play it with the sheet music? From memory? Can they keep a steady beat? Can they play it faster? Slower? Can they sing and play at the same time? Keep mixing up your musical practice with these 8 chapters worth of songs and videos until the answer for most of those questions is a strong yes!

5. If you have some basic piano knowledge, the curriculum is of course playable on the piano. Even if you don't have piano knowledge, you can still use the books and videos, but some of the songs are bell-specific arrangements of songs that are not 100% piano-optimized. The curriculum works great on xylophones and other metallophones, and a new instrument is always a fun way to re-inspire musical play.

This book and the 8 Chapter videos also include a slightly more advanced rhythm method at the end. This works as a comprehensive review of rhythms. It's a bit longer, but if your learners have the attention span, these lessons and videos are a great way to advance your child's understanding of rhythms. Plus, the format is different from Sweet Beets, so your learners might even find it easier. For more information, look for the Rhythm Tree section in the back of this book!

And then, once you've really made the most out of all of the content here in Preschool Prodigies, move onto Psp Melodies or Primary Prodigies.

From our family to yours, we hope you enjoyed Preschool Prodigies. The fun is just beginning inside the Prodigies Playground and we hope to see you in Primary Prodigies and beyond! Thanks again for being here, congratulations on making it this far, and I will C ya later!

– Mr. Rob & the Prodigies Team

Chapter 8 ✿ Section 1: Hand-Sign Review ✿ Lesson Guide

Objective

By the end of this section, students should be able to perform all 8 Solfège hand-signs.

Overview

In this section, students study the elements of all 8 hand-signs.

Essential Question

How can a student refer to the C Major scale using Solfège hand-signs?

Instruction Tips

Hang the hand-sign poster in your music practice space as a way to reference the hand-signs during the videos and activities in this chapter.

Materials

- Full set of C Major deskbells
- Full set of crayons
- Hand-Sign Review Video Access
- Workbook pages: 7-21
- Scissors
- Glue or tape

Table of Contents

Complementary Activities

Put your students in pairs, and tell them to make up a secret hand shake together that involves at least five of the hand-signs. Students should practice this hand shake until they each have it memorized.

Section 8. 1 Video Annotations

0:00 Explain to students that in this video, students will practice hand-signs instead of playing the bells. This chapter will be a review of the Solfège hand-signs.

2:37 Mr. Rob reviews the C Major scale pattern and low do and high do.

At the end ask your learner to perform all eight hand-signs. If they have any trouble, replay this video to review.

Solfège Hand-Sign Review
Lesson 8.1

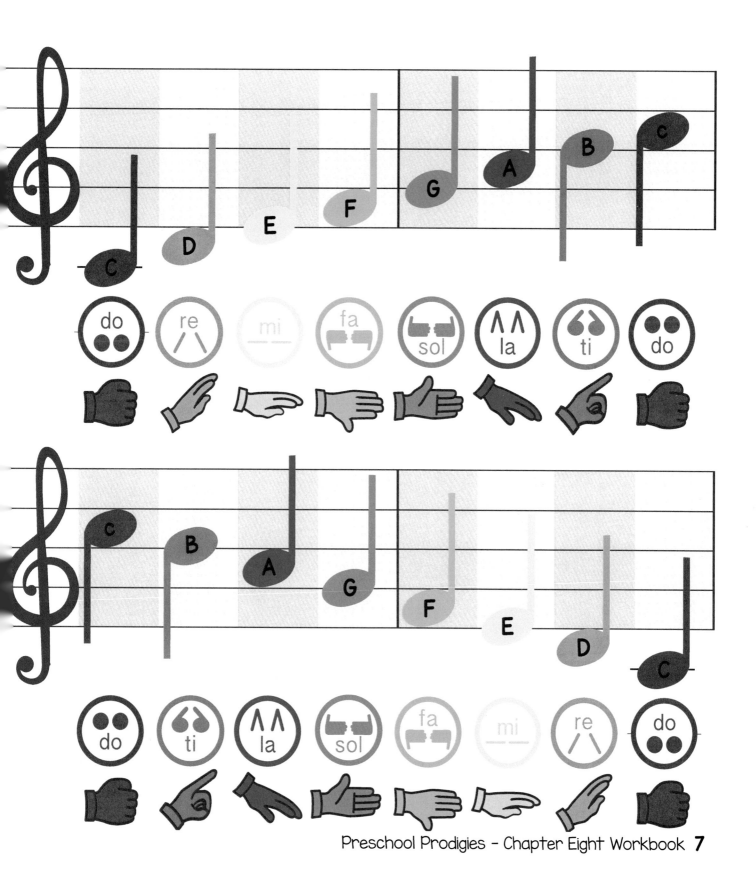

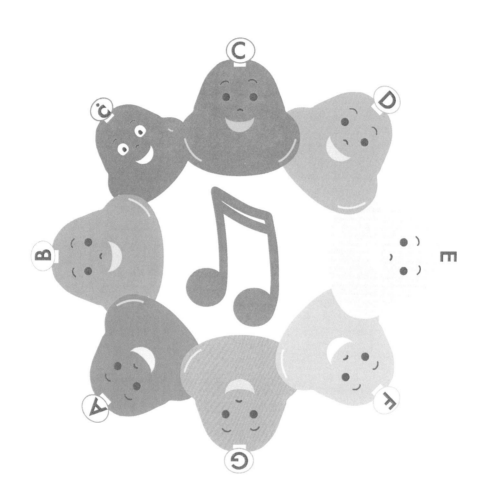

SOLFÈGE HAND SIGNS

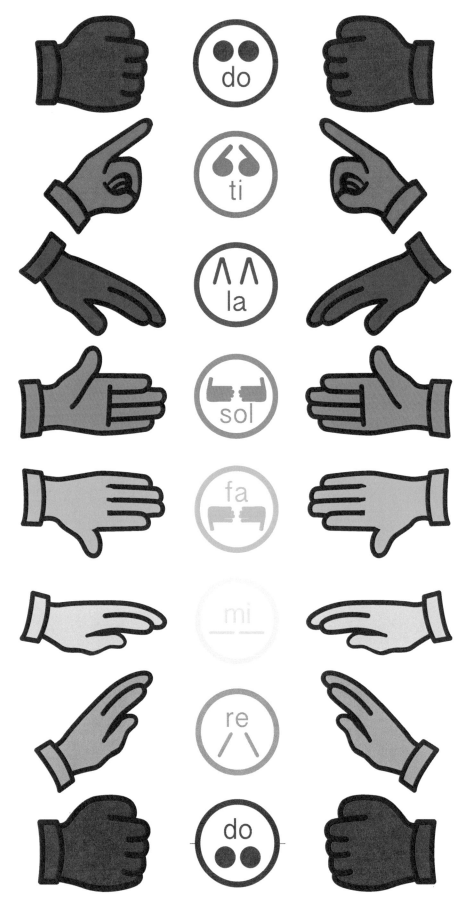

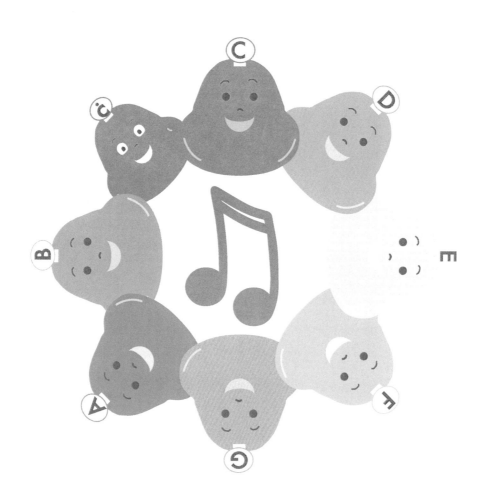

Solfège Matching

Can you match the Solfège hand-signs with the proper hand position?

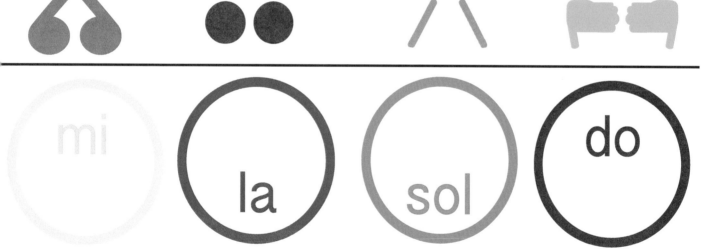

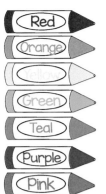

Red
Orange
Yellow
Green
Teal
Purple
Pink

Steps and Sequence

Trace the Solfège name for each note,
then color the number that goes with each one!
Be sure to use each note's matching bell color.

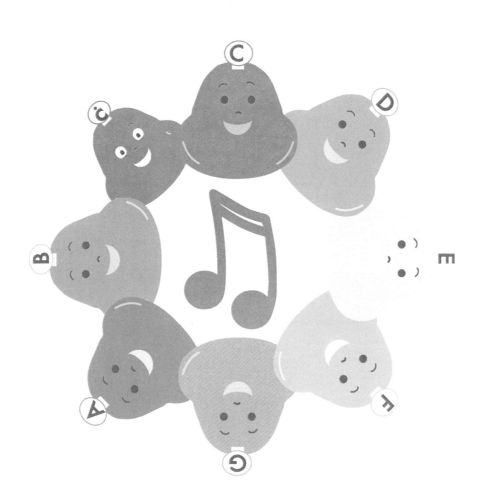

Musical Memory

On the next four pages, cut out the Solfège Hand-Sign cards. Then lay them face
down. Taking turns, turn over 2 cards. If they match, keep those cards!
If they don't, turn the cards over and let the next player try.
Use your memory to find the cards! And for some added fun, sing and hand-signs as
you turn over the cards.

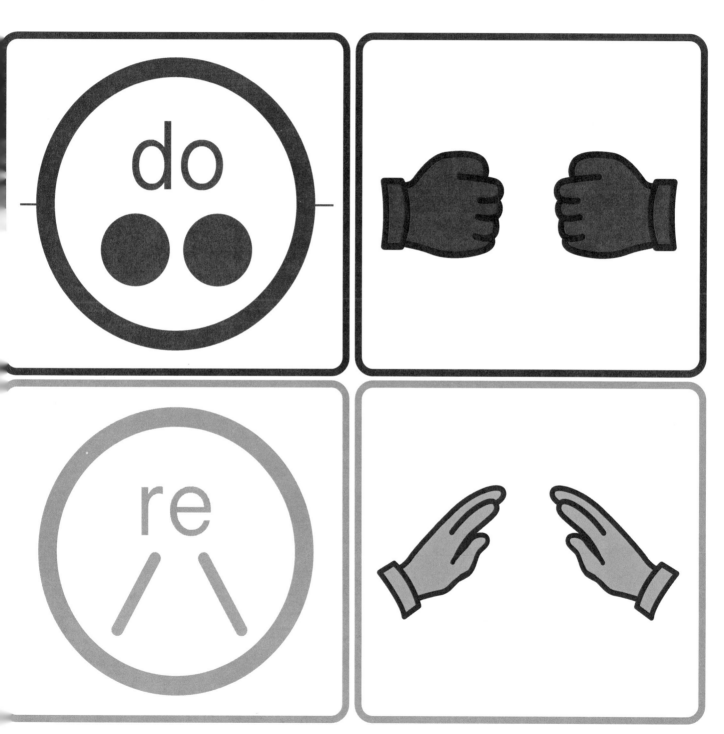

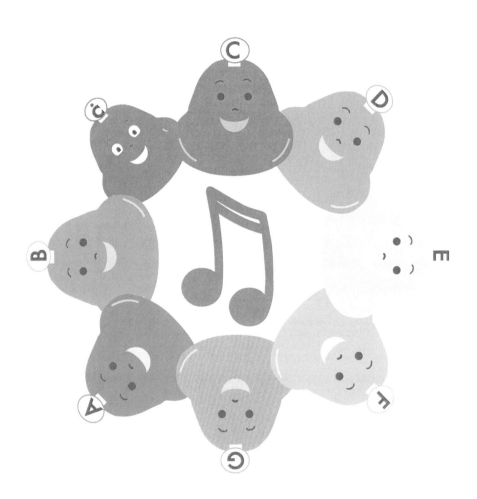

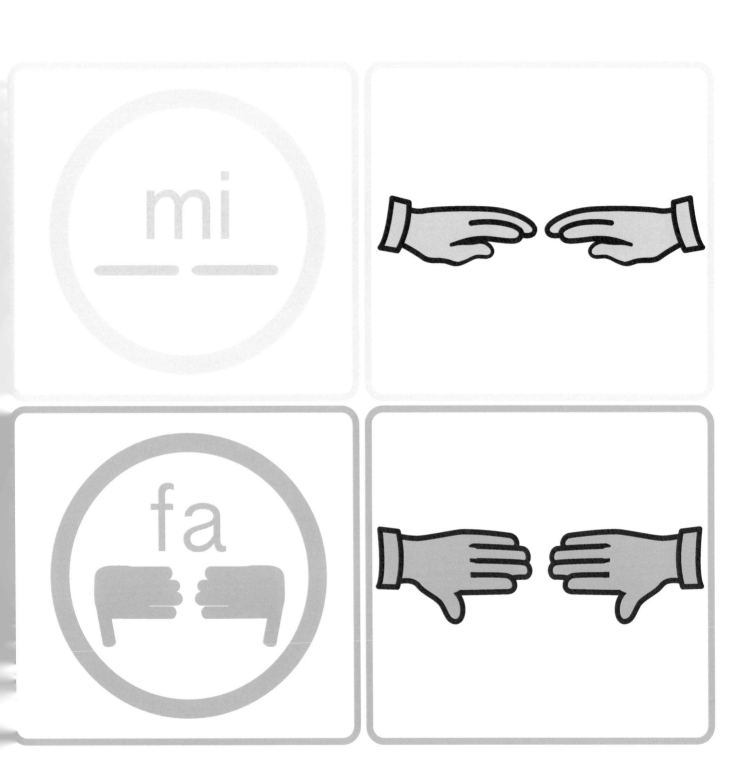

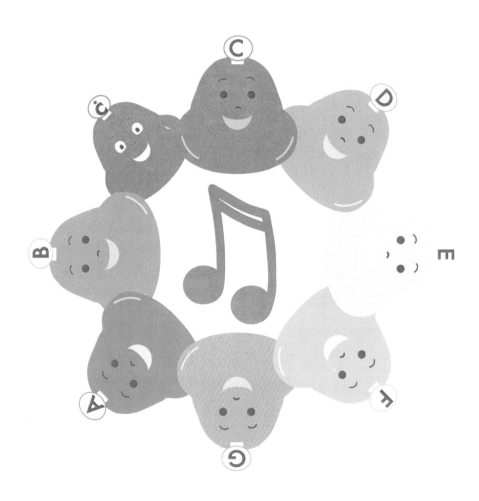

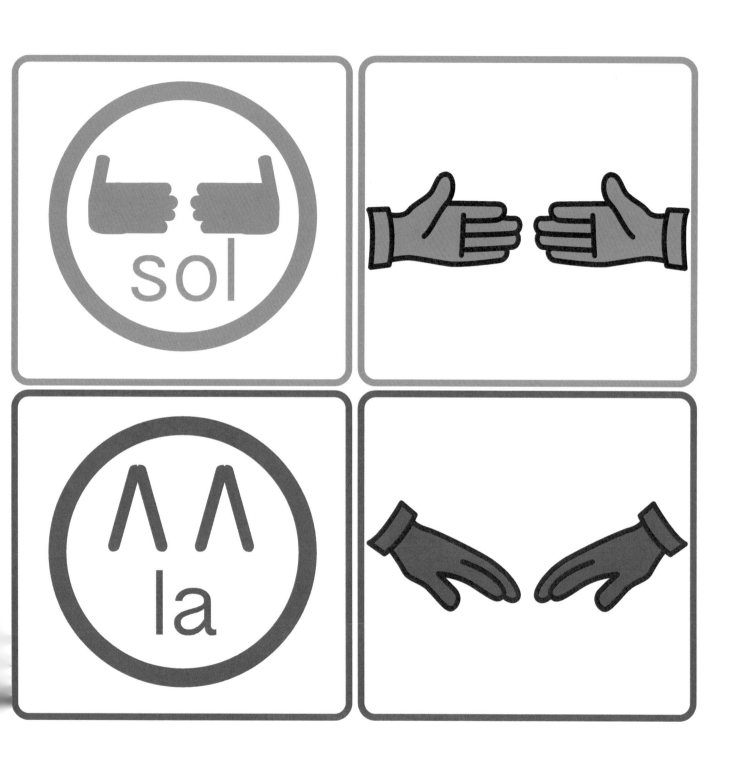

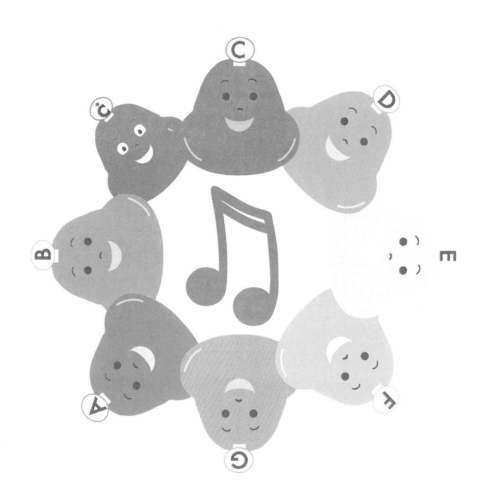

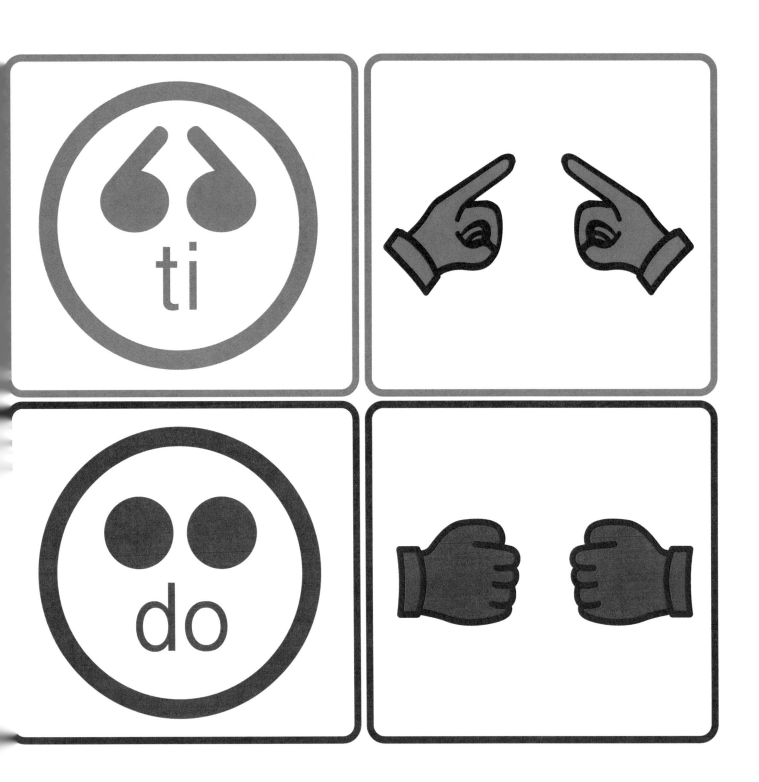

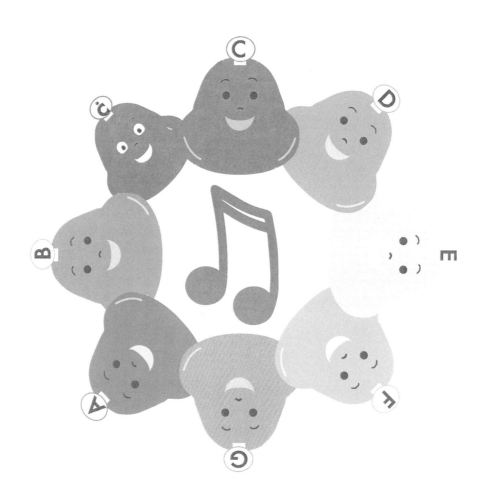

Chapter 8 ♫ Section 2: Hand Sign Compilation ♫ Lesson Guide

Objective

By the end of this section, students should be able to describe all eight notes using numbers, notes, adjectives and hand-signs.

Overview

In this section, students practice matching each of the Solfège hand-signs to adjectives, numbers, and notes.

Essential Question

How can a student describe the notes of the C Major Scale?

Instruction Tips

Since students are hand-signing a lot in this section, make sure they are playing their bells before and after completing each activity. This will help reinfornce the assocation of each note and hand-sign.

Materials

- Full Set of Deskbells
- Full Set of Crayons
- Hand-Sign Compilation Video Access
- Workbook pages: 24-41

Table of Contents

Complementary Activities

Use the songbooks in the Playground to continue guessing song titles just by hand-signing. Sing and hand-sign one of the songs in the Prodigies Songbook, and let your learner guess which one it is.

Section 8.2 Video Annotations

0:00 Explain to students that in this video they will sing and hand-sign along with Mr. Rob, and see if they can identify the title of the song without hearing the lyrics.

1:08 Mr. Rob begins "Mary Had a Little Lamb".

1:47 Pause here and let your learners guess what song it is before Mr. Rob reveals it.

2:13 Mr. Rob begings "Jingle Bells".

3:49 Mr. Rob begins "Row your Boat".

4:43 Mr. Rob begins "Twinkle Twinkle Little Star".

6:18 Mr. Rob begins "Are you Sleeping".

What Song is This?

Below are some verses from several songs that we've studied in the Playground. Sing the hand-signs below, and try to guess the song, then write the name in the box.

Song Title

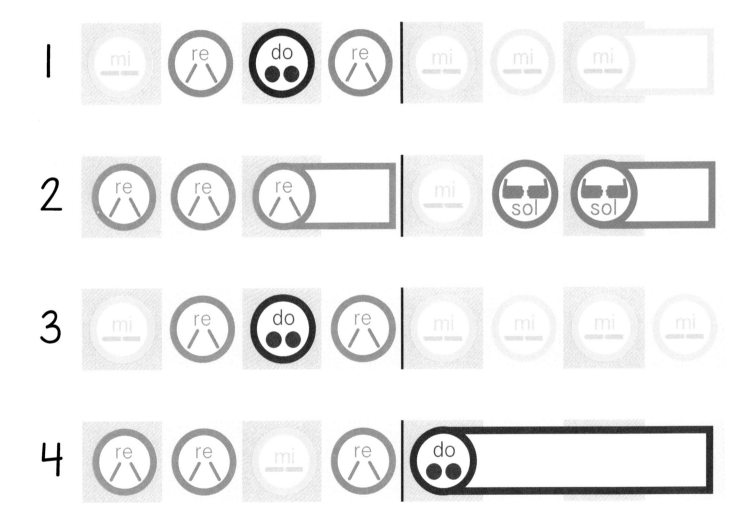

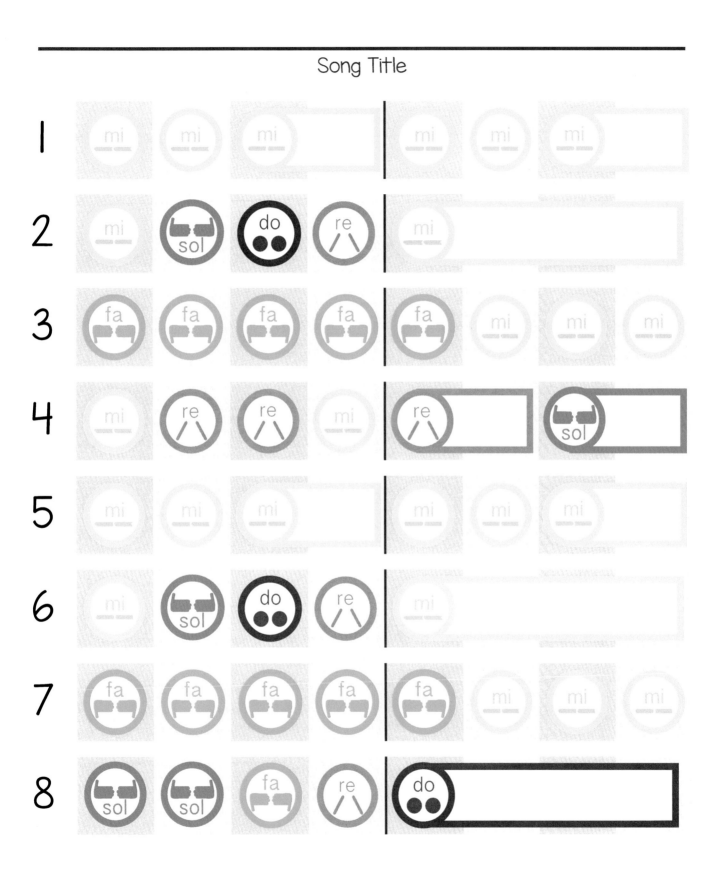

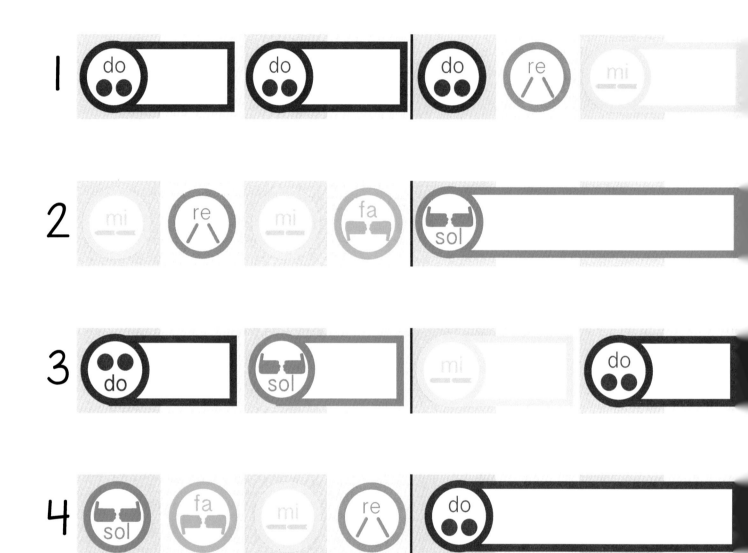

1

2

3

4

Repeat one more time!

Song Title

1

2

3

4

5

6

Song Title

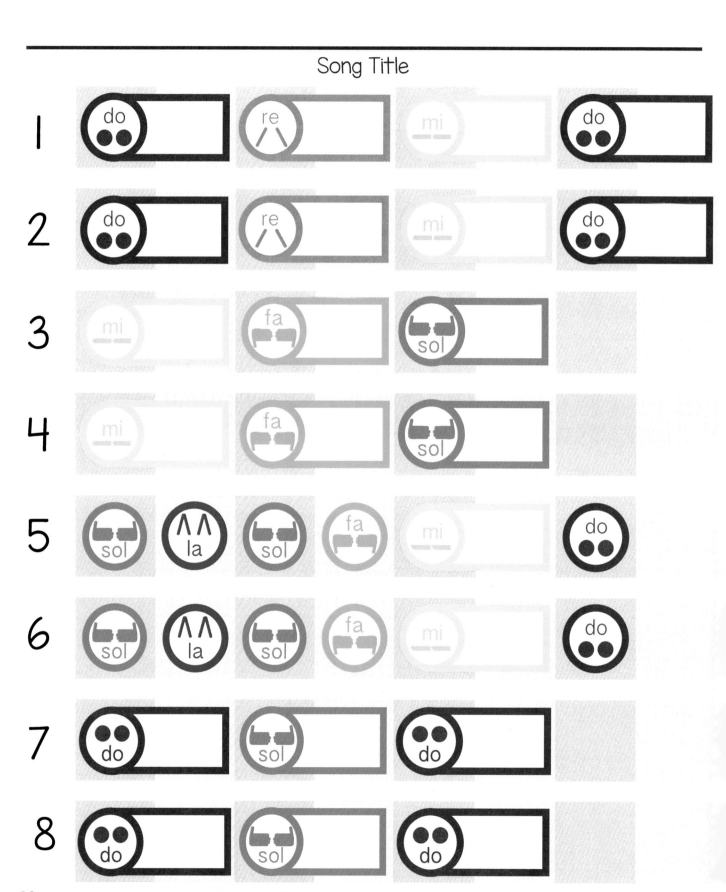

Match the Hand-Signs

Connect the hand-signs in the middle to the and the numbers on the outisde.

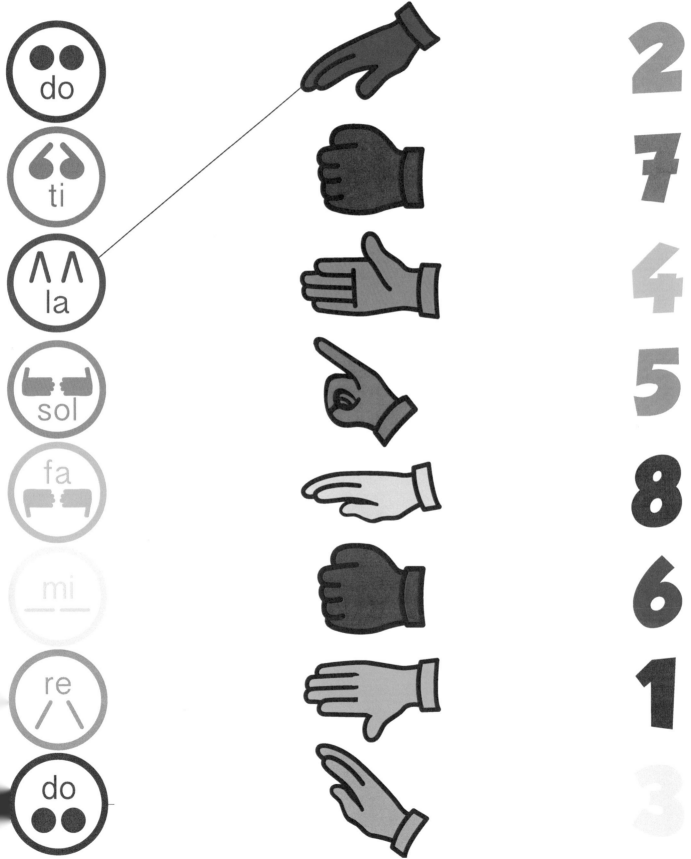

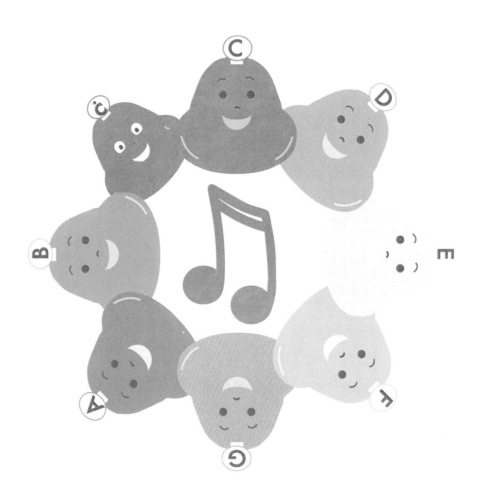

Musical Feelings

We talked a little bit about the feelings of the Solfège Hand Signs in the first video of the Chapter. Now that we've sang some more songs with the hand-signs, let's talk a bit more about the musical feelings!

The different musical notes bring out different feelings when we play them.
It's not exactly the same for every person, but it's usually not far off.
Imagine you want to paint a picture of sky. You'll need some blue paint, or maybe some orange to paint a sky at sunset.
Now imagine you want to make a happy song. You'll need some Do, Mi, Sol or some Fa, La, Do.
Imagine you want your melody to be bright and playful – you'll need some Sol and La.
Or if you want it to be restful, try some Mi and Do.
It's not always the same for everyone...what do you think the notes sound like?

Cut out the following cards and use them to create songs, stories, melodies and chords!

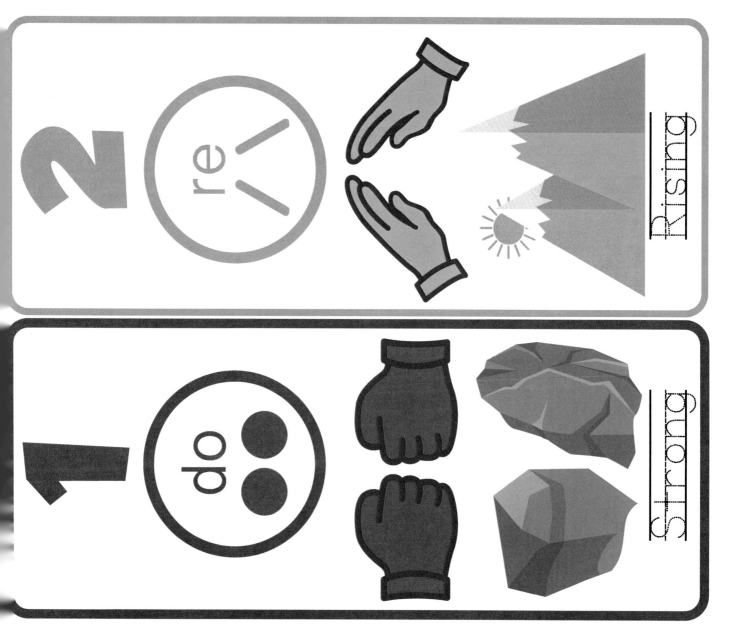

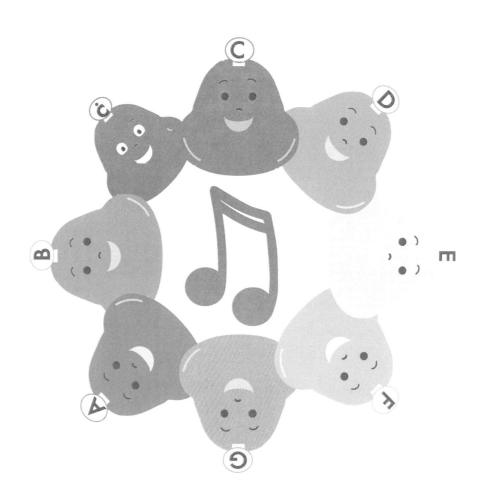

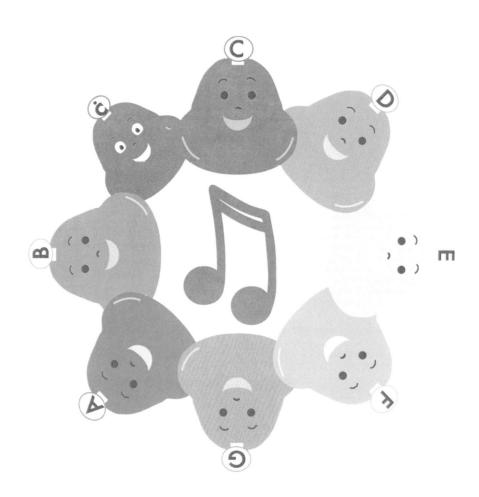

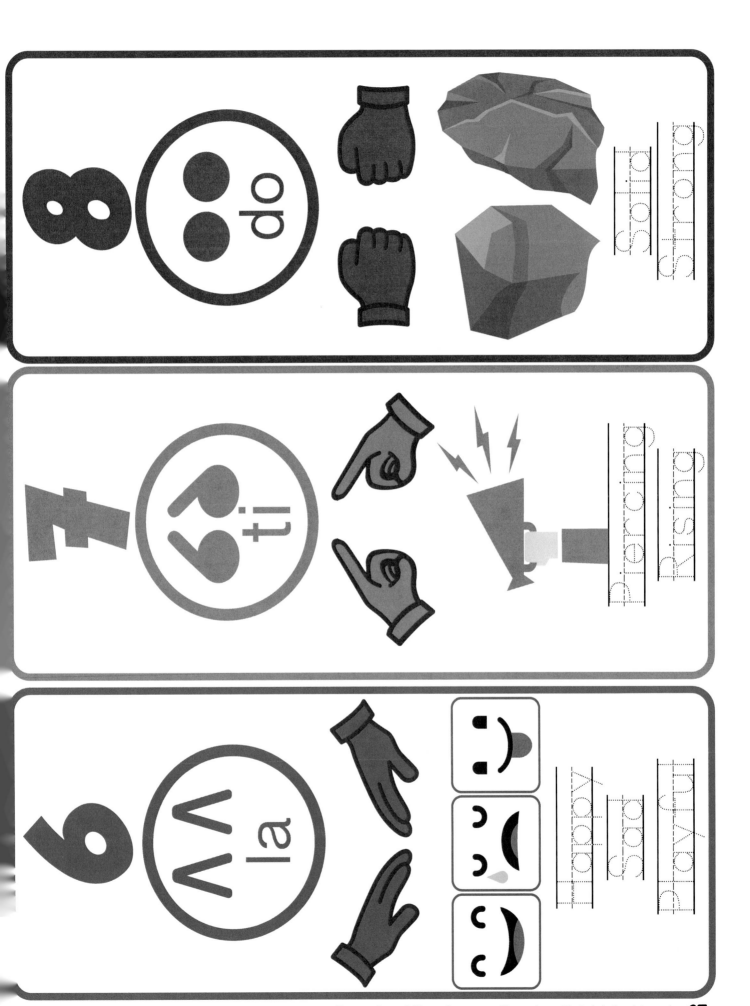

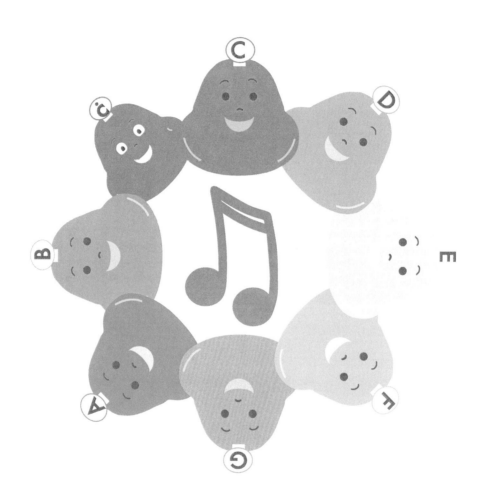

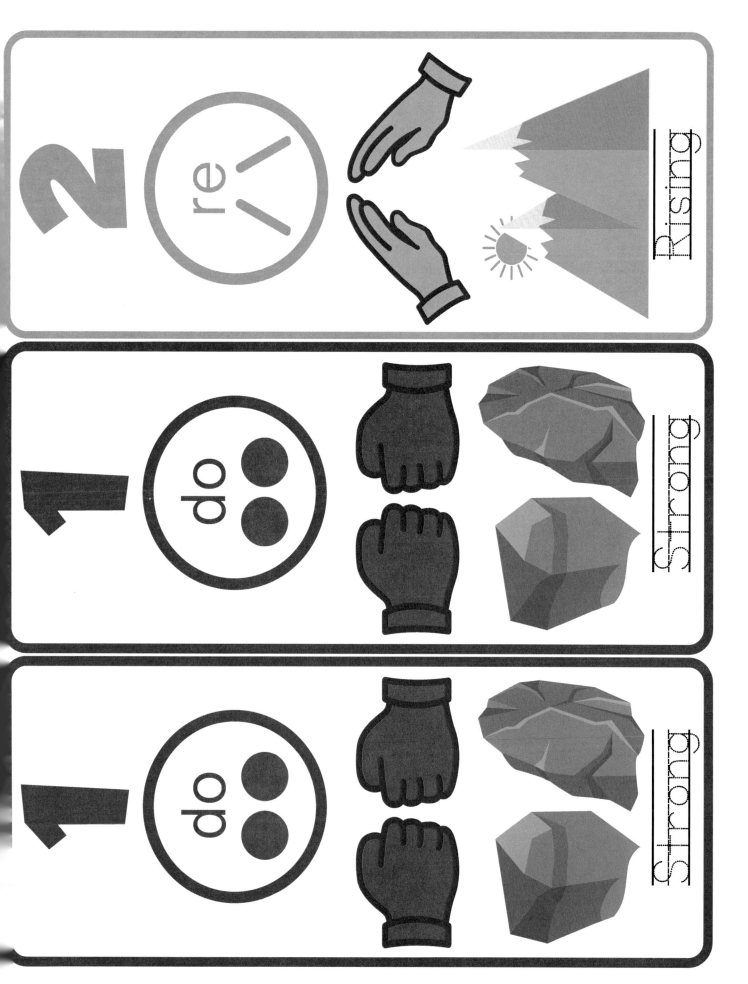

2   re

Rising

1   do

Strong

1   do

Strong

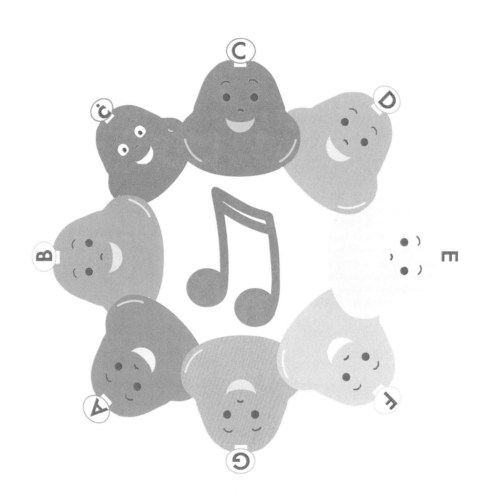

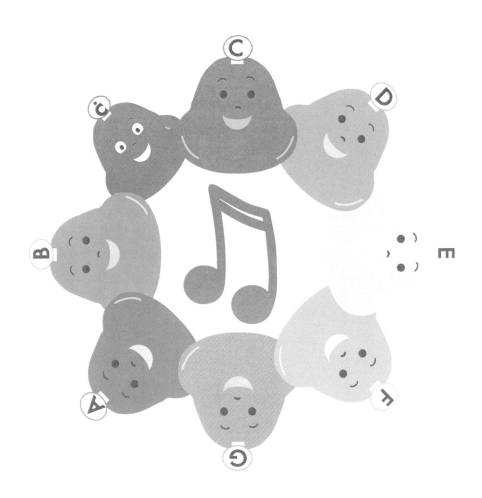

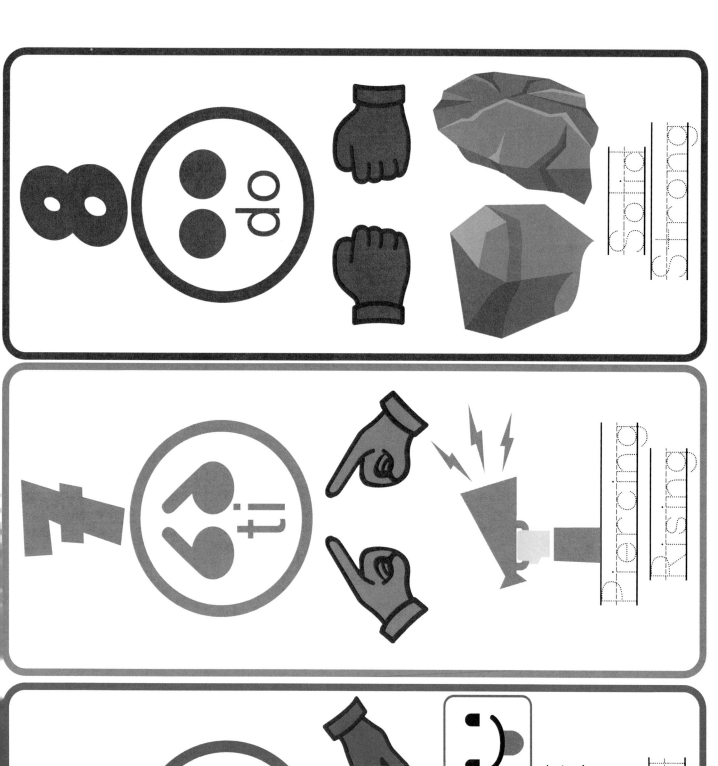

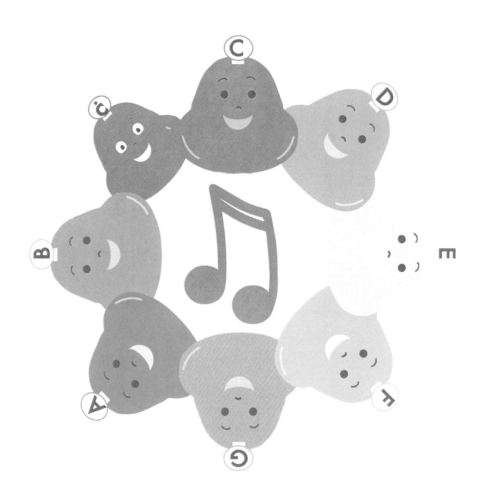

Chapter 8 ❧ Section 3: Skidamarink ❧ Lesson Guide

Objective

By the end of this section, students should be able to play "Skidamarink".

Overview

In this section, students play and study a simplified version of the song "Skidamarink".

Essential Question

How can a student play "Skidamarink"?

Instruction Tips

If students struggle to write their own lyrics to "Skidamarink", try giving them a topic like things to do at school, habits and daily routines, or even just the letters of their name.

Materials

- C Bell • D Bell • E Bell • G Bell
- A Bell • B Bell • c Bell
- Full Set of Crayons
- Skidamarink Video Access
- Workbook pages: 44-51

Table of Contents

Complementary Activities

Ask students to sing their new lyrics for the class or a partner. Alternatively, give the whole class a topic and challenge them to write a song together or in pairs to the tune of "Skidamarink".

Section 8.3 Video Annotations

1:38 Mr. Rob switches from singing the colors of the bells and playing to singing the Solfège names and hand-signing.

2:23 Mr. Rob switches from singing the Solfège names and hand-signing and sings the lyrics to "Skidamarink".

3:33 Mr. Rob explains falsetto voice and the difference between singing high and low.

Skidamarink

Lesson 8.3

☆☆☆☆☆

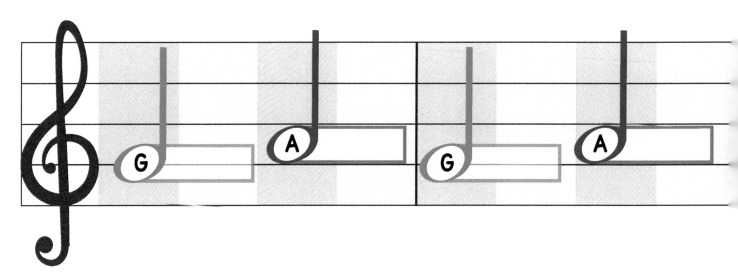

1. Skidamarink e-dink-e-dink, Skidamarink e-doo,

2.

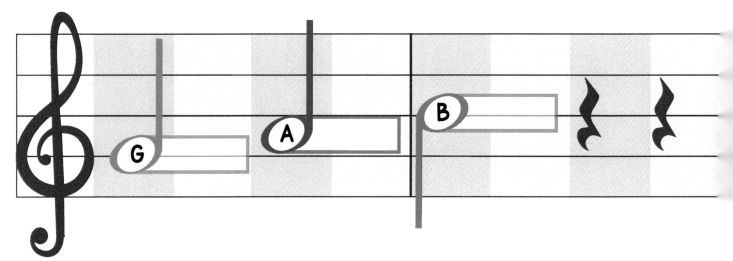

I　　　love　　　you.

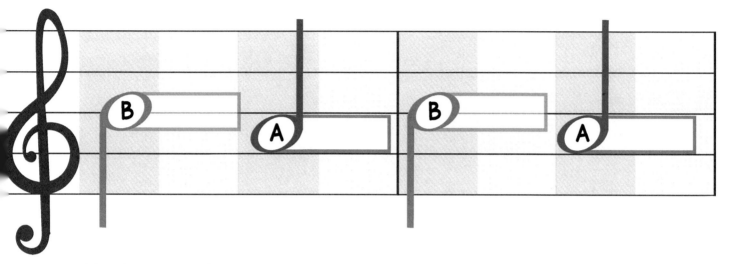

Skidamarink e-dink-e-dink, Skidamarink e-doo,

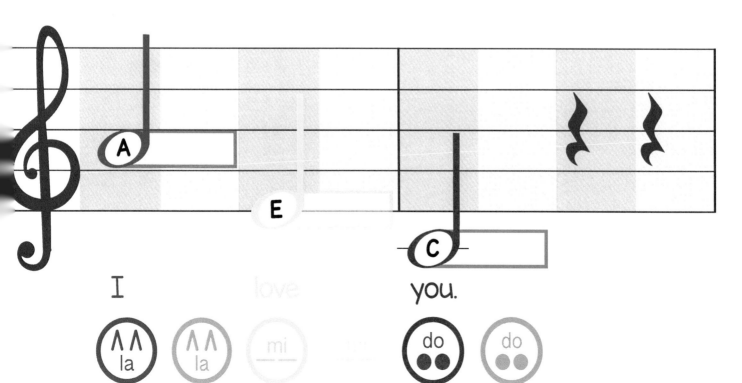

I love you.

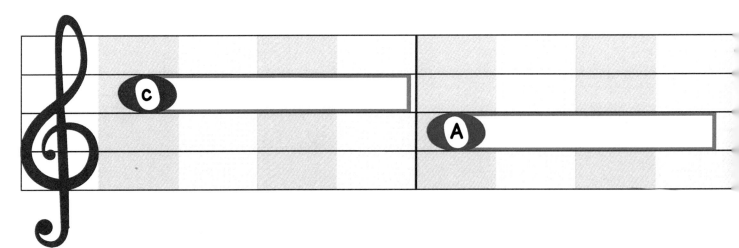

Well, I love you in the morning and in the afternoon,

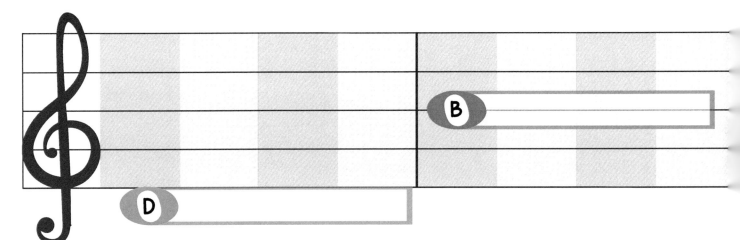

I love you in the evening and underneath the moon.

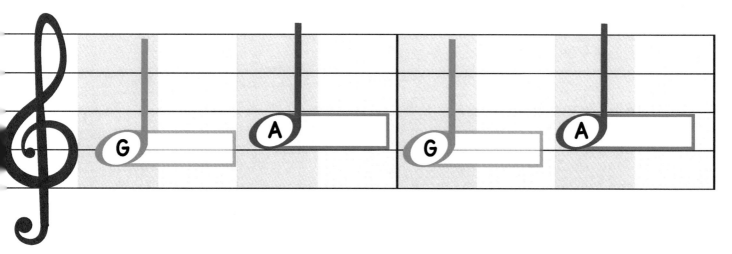

1. Skidamarink e-dink-e-dink, Skidamarink e-doo,

2.

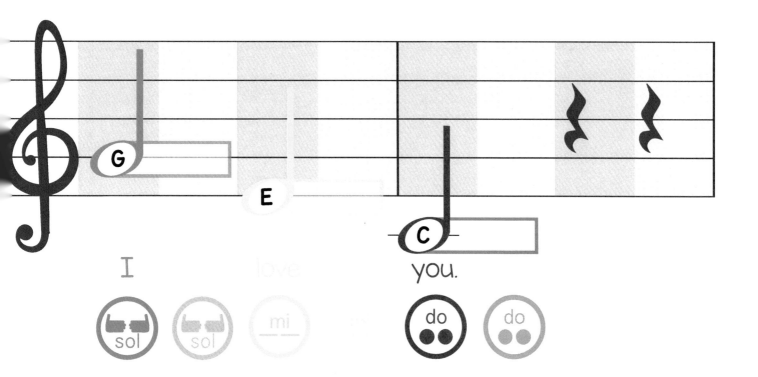

I love you.

Write New Lyrics

Skidamarink is a funny word that doesn't really mean anything.
Write your own song full of funny words to the tune of Skidamarink!

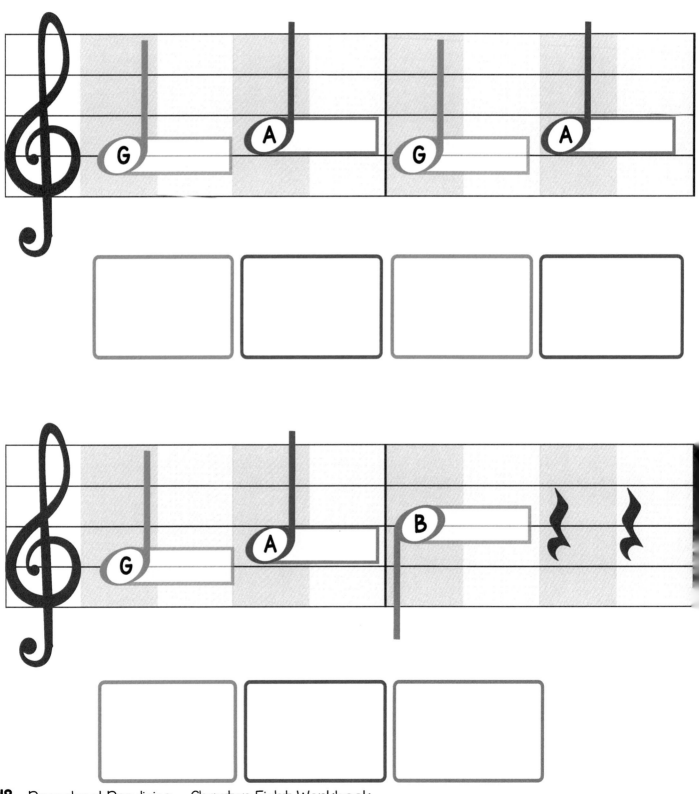

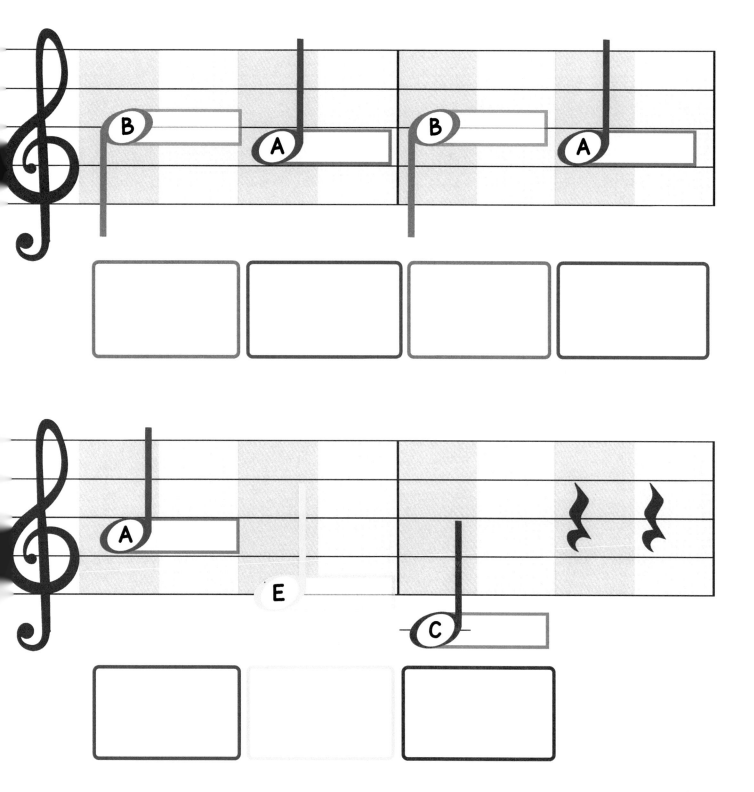

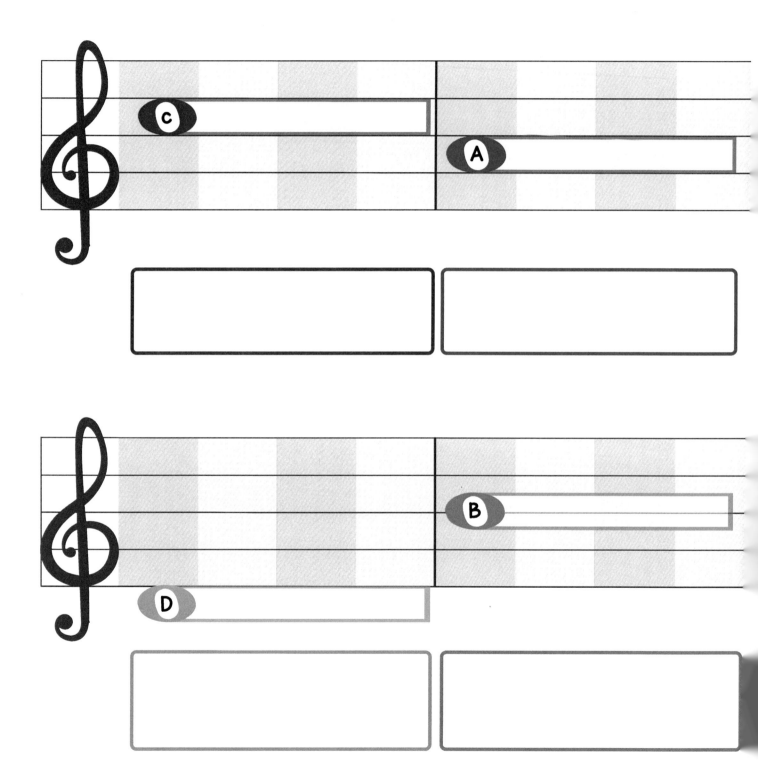

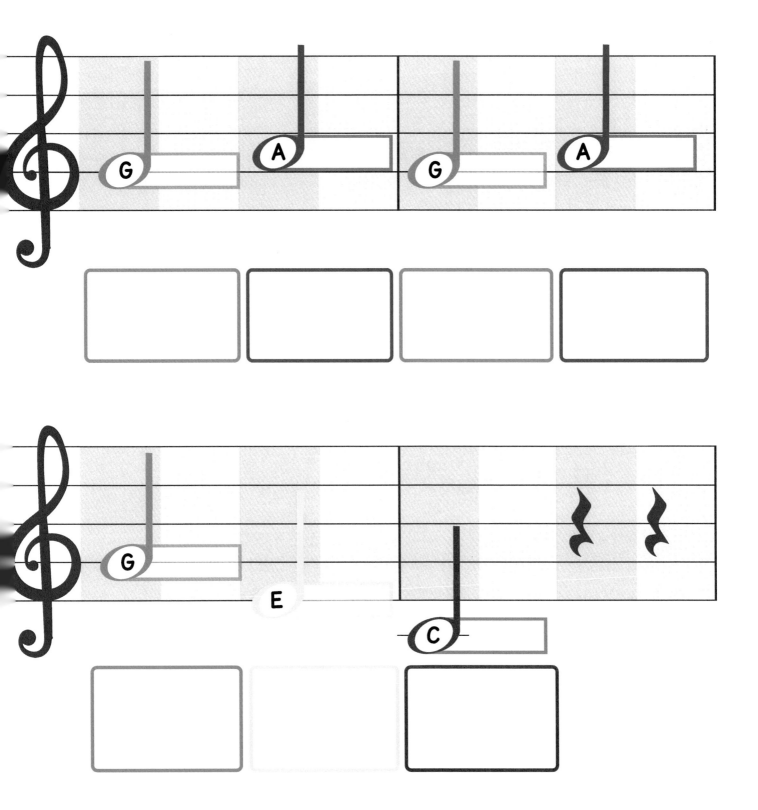

Note Hearts

Get some crayons or colored pencils – it's coloring time.
Use the colors of the bells and color in each heart with the matching color.

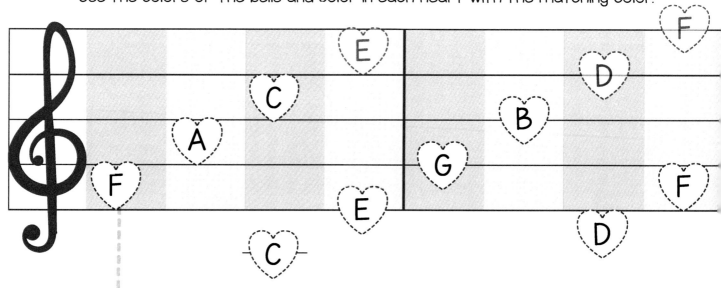

Write the letter names in the hearts! Hint: copy the letters from the music above

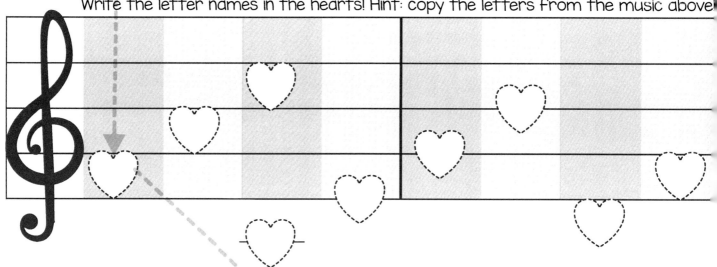

Challenge: Try the same activity with the simple pattern below.
Hint: Look at the different lines and spaces. Also, use the notes above to help.

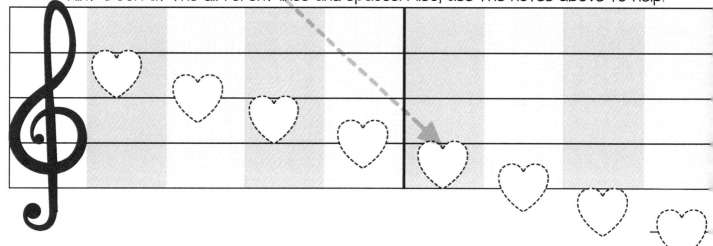

Chapter 8 🎵 Section R: Sweet Beets #7 🎵 Lesson Guide

Objective

By the end of this section, students will be able to sing Sweet Beets using tas, ti-tis and tika tikas.

Overview

In this section, students use tas, ti-tis and tika tikas to count rhythm.

Essential Question

How can a student use a variety of rhythms to sing "Sweet Beets"?

Instruction Tips

Before watching the video, cut out the rhythmic blocks activities iat the end of this book to place along with Mr. Rob in the video.

Materials

- Red Crayon
- Sweet Beets #7 Video Access
- Workbook pages: 54-59

Table of Contents

Complementary Activities

Play a call and response pattern using ta, ti-ti and tika tika. Pause the video and allow students to make up their own call & response rhythm sections in Sweet Beets.

Section 8.R Video Annotations

0:34 This is a good place to have students take out their rhythm cards--either the red block ta or the beet/quarter note card.

1:10 This is a good place to have students take out their rhythm cards--either the yellow ti-tis or the cherry/eighth note card.

1:56 This is a good place to have students take out their rhythm cards--either the orange tika tikas or the avocado/sixteenth note card.

4:26 Sweet Beets begins.

Ta, Ti-Ti and Tika-Tika
Lesson 8.R
☆☆☆☆☆

Clap, tap or stomp along while you sing with the sheet music below after you've watched the Beet & Avocado video in section 7.R.

CHORUS 1

Sweet Beets, we've got some!
If you **want some** Sweet Beets, we've got 'em.
If you want Sweet Beets, we've got some,
If you **want some** Sweet Beets, we've got 'em.

VERSE 1

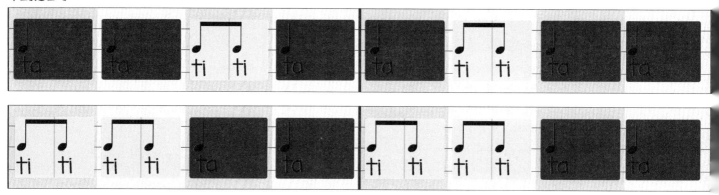

CHORUS 2: REPEAT CHORUS 1

VERSE 1

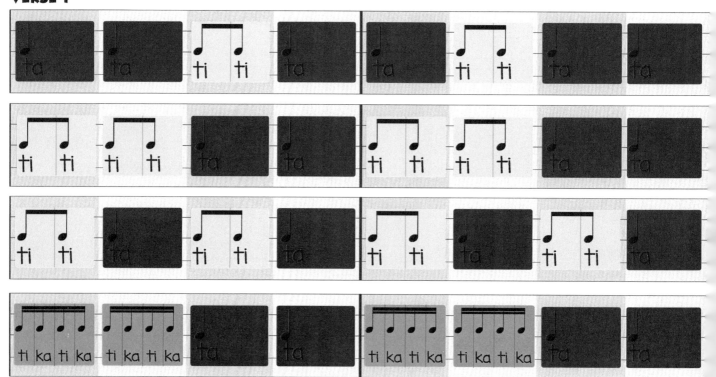

VERSE 3

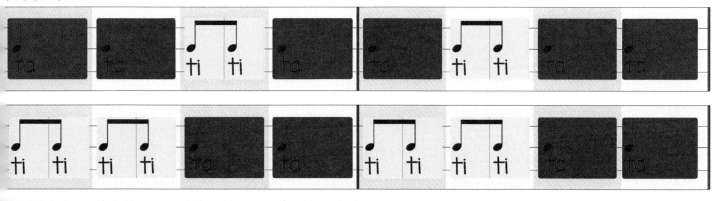

CHORUS 3: REPEAT CHORUS 1

VERSE 4

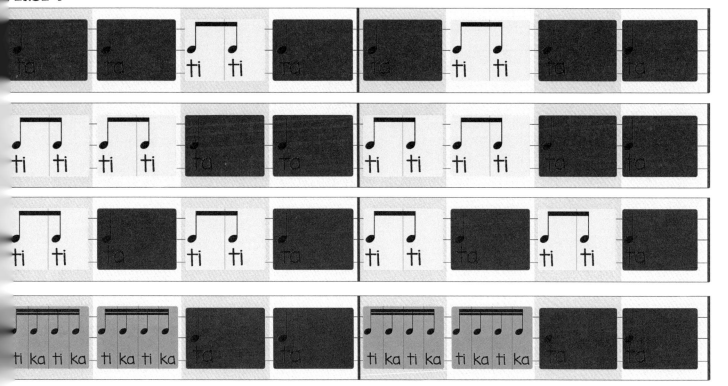

CHORUS 4

Sweet Beets, we've got some!
If you **want some** Sweet Beets, we've got 'em.
If you want Sweet Beets, we've got some,
If you **want some** Sweet Beets, we've got 'em.

Finish the Pattern

Finish each line of the pattern using Ta, Ti-Ti and Tika-Tika.

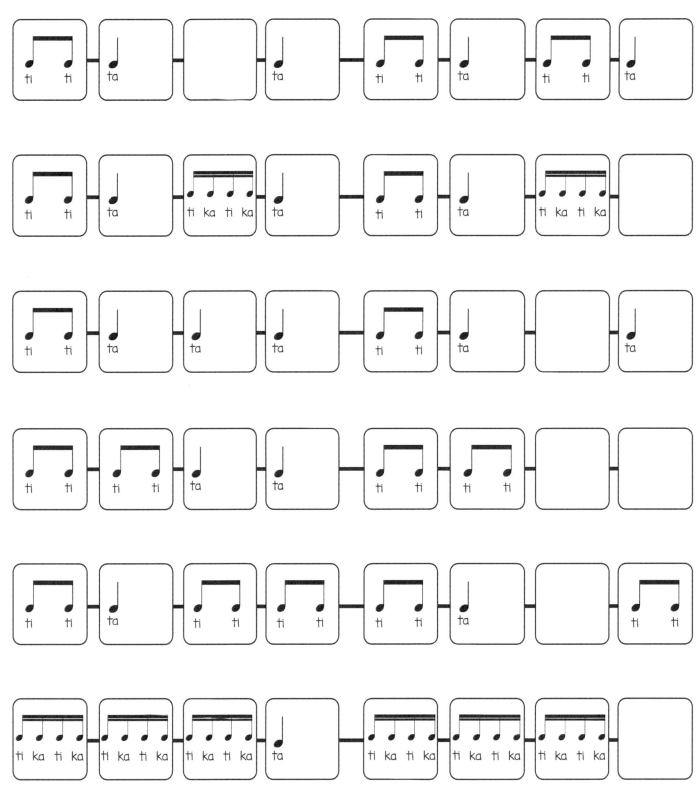

Rhythm Vocab

Connect the images in the left to the matching ones on the right.

REPEAT

1 MEASURE

ti ka ti ka

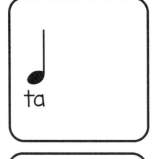

ta

ti   ti

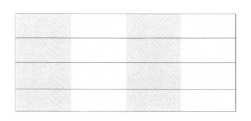

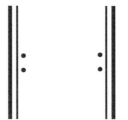

Missing Notes

Some of the measures below are missing notes. Draw quarter notes to help complete the measures below!

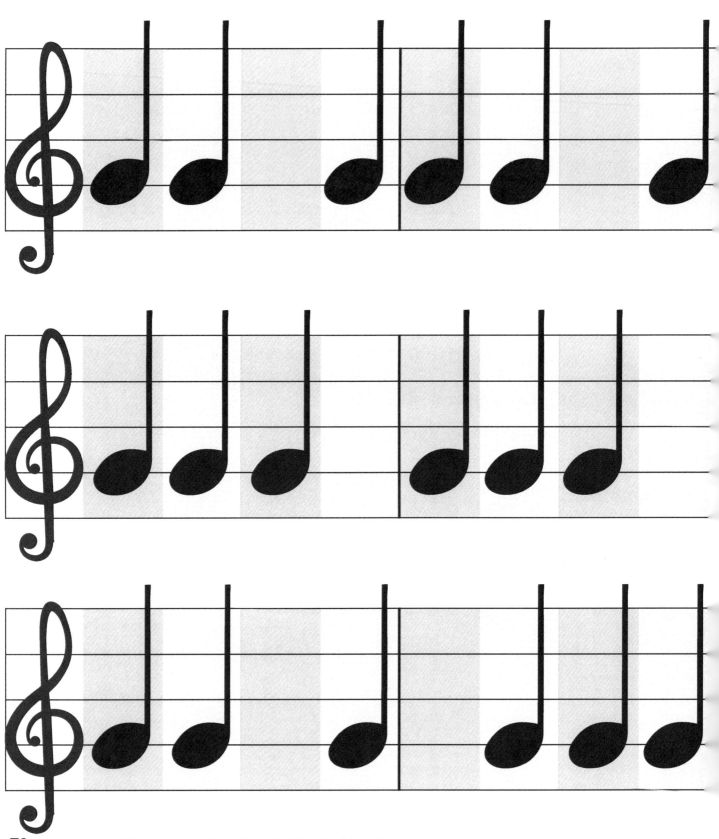

♪♪ Adding Eighths ♪♪

Adding up the eighth notes can be tricky. We tried a little in Chapter 7, but let's review.

Don't forget that it takes TWO eighth notes to fill up one beat. = ♩ = 1 Beat

We can write our eighth notes together, or we can split them up like this ♪♪

It might seem hard, but don't worry. Just focus on circling PAIRS of eighth notes.

Then count how many circles you have!

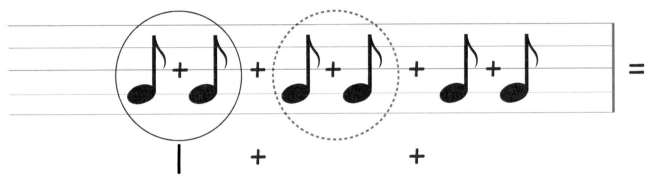

Chapter 8 ❀ Section 4: Happy Birthday ❀ Lesson Guide

Objective

By the end of this section, students should be able to play "Happy Birthday".

Overview

In this section, students play "Happy Birthday" and review musical skips.

Essential Question

How can a student play "Happy Birthday"?

Instruction Tips

Use actual books or steps to make physcial tiers for the Musical Steps & Skips activity. Use this as a reference to help students visualize the amount of space between each note.

Materials

- D Bell • E Bell • F Bell
- G Bell • A Bell • B Bell • c Bell
- Full Set of Crayons
- Happy Birthday Video Access
- Workbook pages: 62-68

Table of Contents

Complementary Activities

Take turns going around the room, singing each student "Happy Birthday". Allow each student to choose whether the class sings and hand-signs or sings and plays the deskbells.

Section 8.4 Video Annotations

0:00 Explain to students that in this video they will play a song using all but low C to play this song, but that they will start with just the hand-signs.

1:25 Students begin playing bells and singing the colors of the song.

2:05 Students begin playing bells and singing the note names of the song.

2:45 Students begin singing the lyrics of the song without playing the bells.

Happy Birthday
Lesson 8.4

☆ ☆ ☆ ☆ ☆

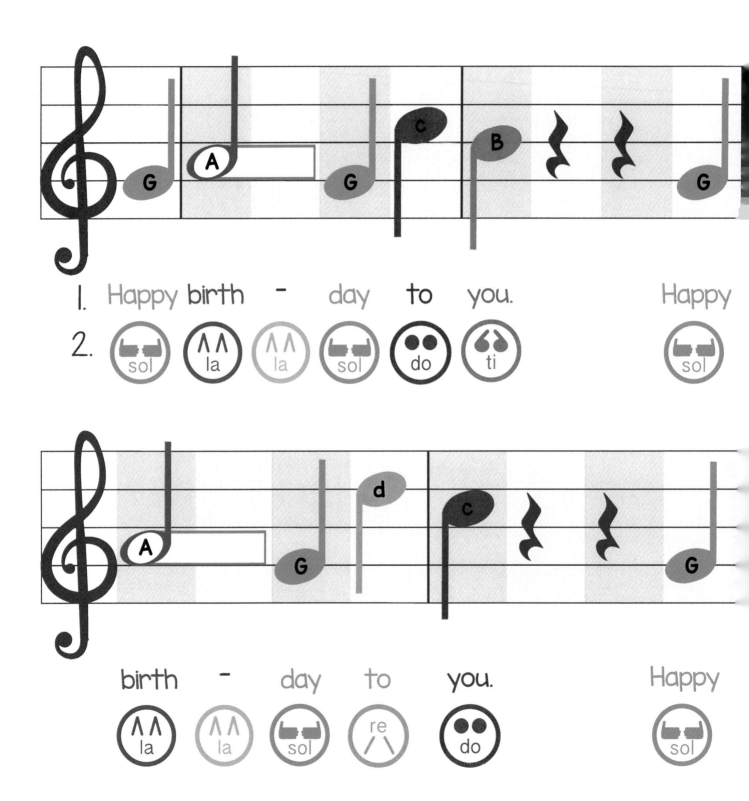

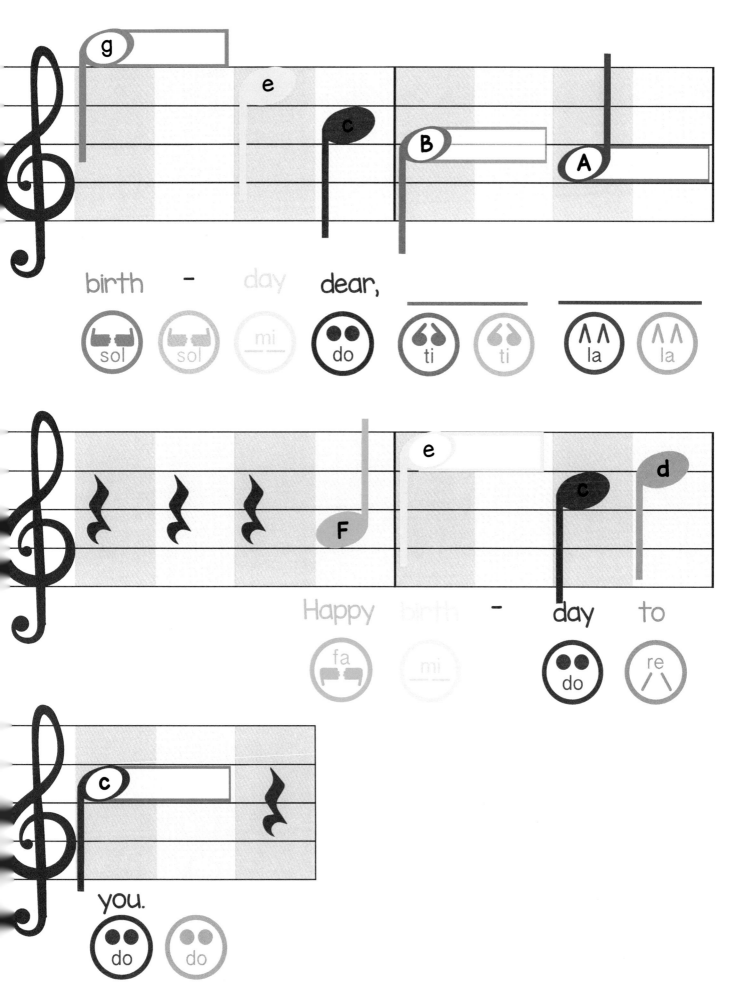

Musical Steps & Skips

The first few skips, steps and sames are written for you.
Draw the skips, steps and same arrows for the whole song!
When you're done, sing with the hand-signs or play your bells with the numbers.

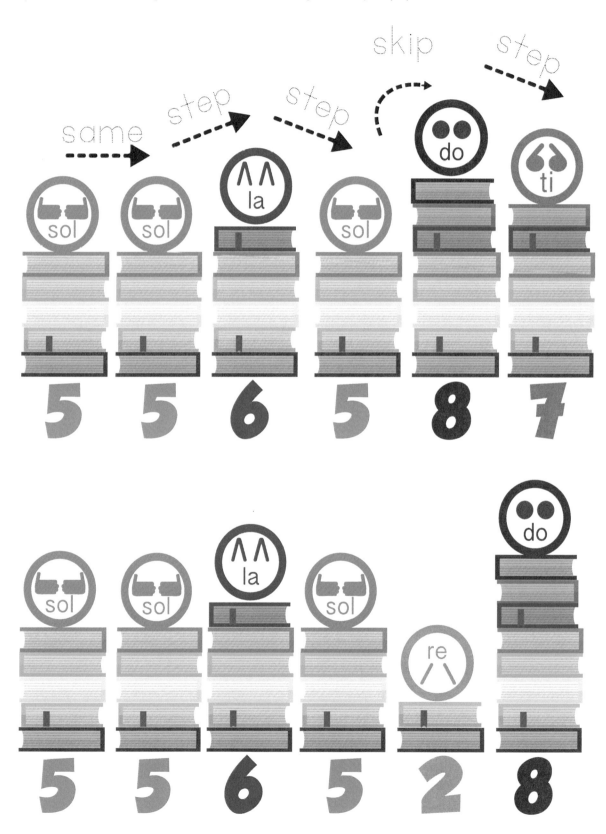

Sheet Music Cakes

Grab your crayons or colored pencils and use the colors of the notes to color in all of the cakes. If any letters are missing write them into the note cakes!

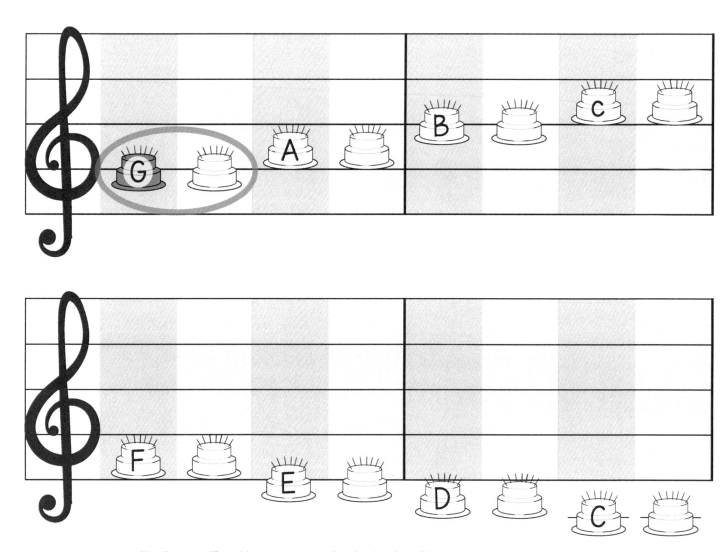

Challenge: Try the same activity but without the letter names.
Hint: Use the different lines and spaces to help.
Also, use the cakes you colored above to help!

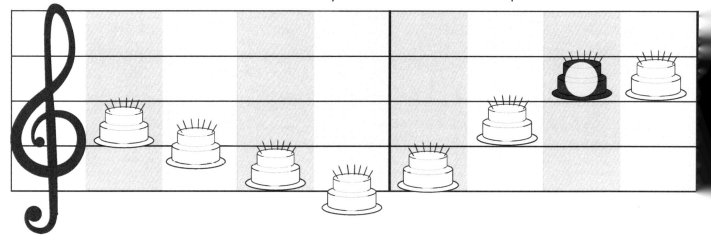

Finish the Pattern

Happy Birthday, Bells!

Draw a line between each bell and its matching balloons.

Chapter 8 ✤ Section 5: Itsy Bitsy Spider ✤ Lesson Guide

Objective

By the end of this section, students should be able to play "Itsy Bitsy Spider".

Overview

In this section, students play and sing "Itsy Bitsy Spider".

Essential Question

How can a student play "Itsy Bitsy Spider" using the C Major Scale?

Instruction Tips

Encourage students to think about the colors if they're having trouble remembering the note names from memory.

Materials

- Full Set of C Major Deskbells
- Full Set of Crayons
- Itsy Bitsy Spider Video Access
- Workbook Pages: 70-78

Table of Contents

Complementary Activities

Put your learners in pairs to write a song together. They could combine the songs they wrote in this section or make up new one from scratch.

Section 8.5 Video Annotations

0:00 Explain to students that in this video they will be playing the "Itsy Bitsy Spider" today using the first five notes.

1:21 Mr. Rob's sings the Solfège names of the each notes as he plays.

1:45 Mr. Rob's sings the scale degrees of the each notes as he plays.

2:16 Mr. Rob's sings the lyrics of "Itsy Bitsy Spider" as he plays.

Itsy Bitsy Spider

Lesson 8.5

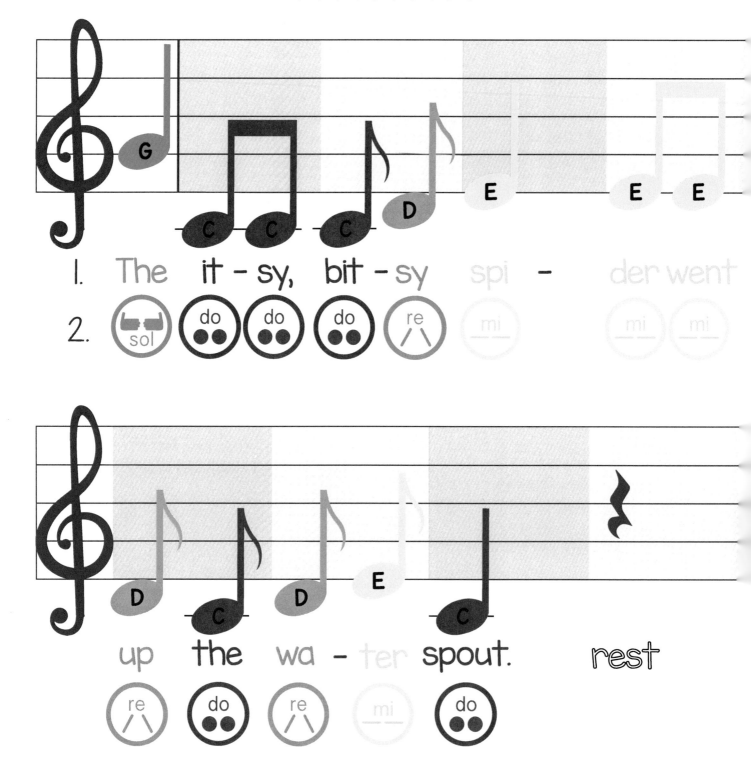

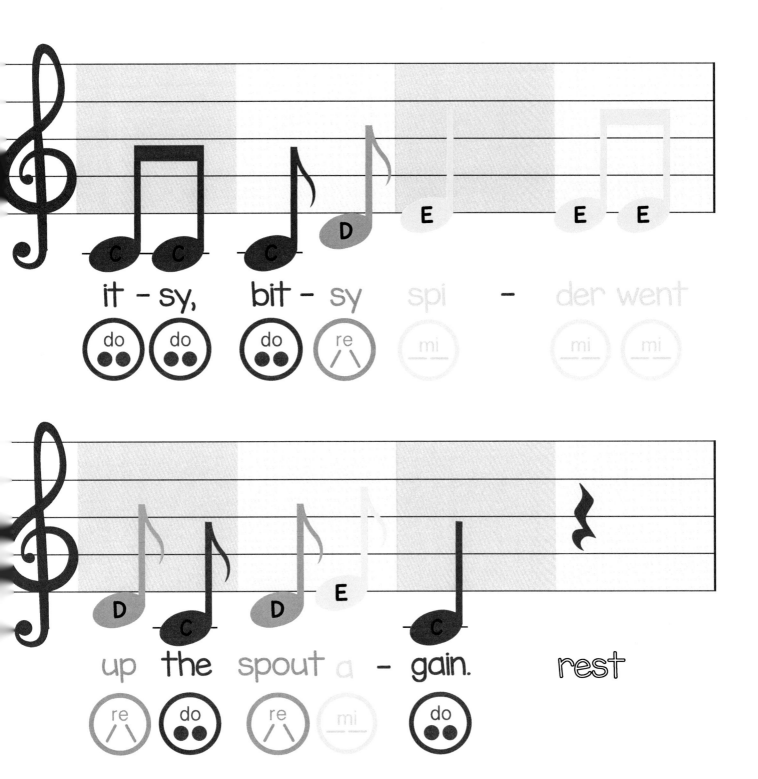

Label the Notes

The note names are missing!! Can you help each note remeber its name?

The   it - sy,   bit - sy   spi - der went

up   the   wa - ter   spout.

Down   came the   rain   to

wash the   spi - der   out.   rest

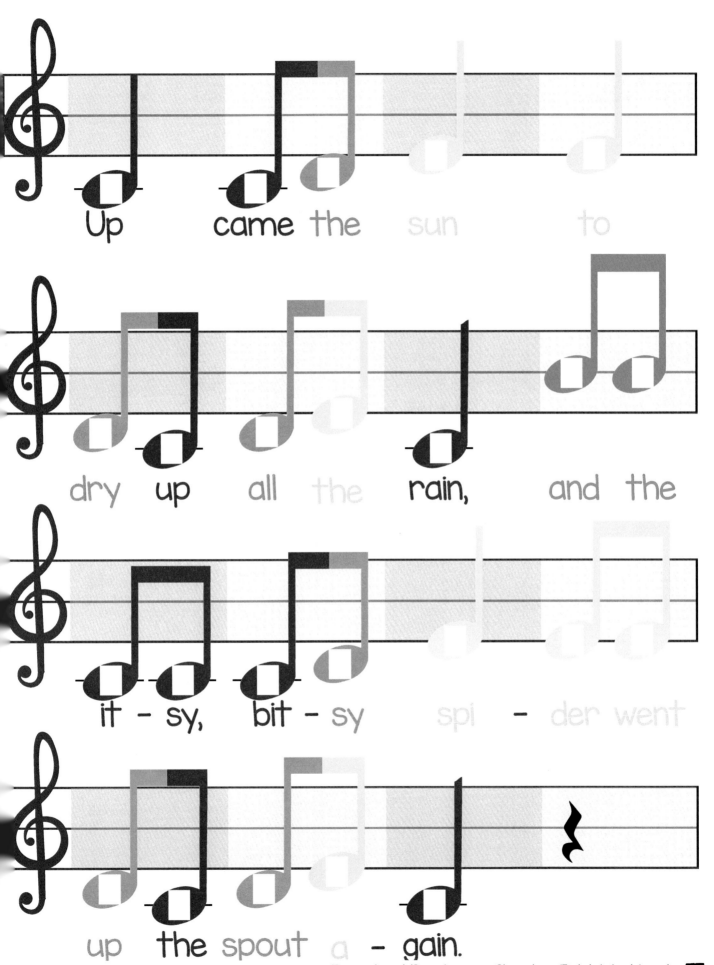

Spider Notes

Grab your crayons or colored pencils and use the colors of the notes to color in all of the spiders. If any letters are missing write them into the spider notes! Then circle any of the same notes that are next to each other!

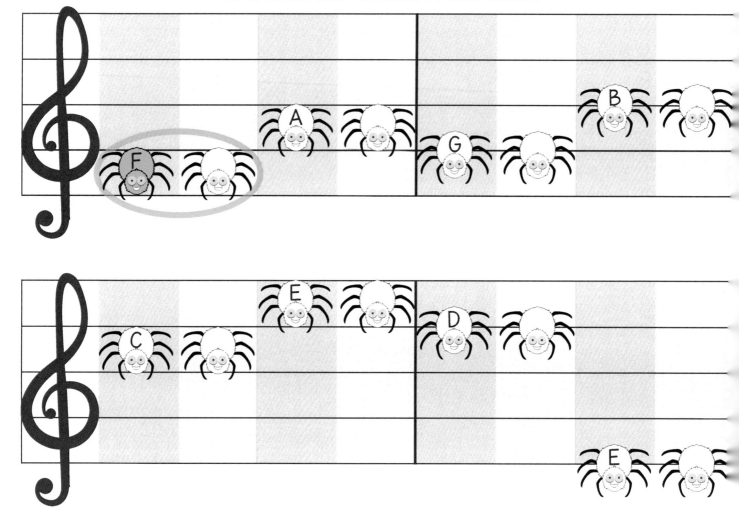

Challenge: Try the same activity but without the letter names.
Hint: Use the different lines and spaces to help.
Also, use the spiders you colored above to help!

Finish the Pattern

Finish each line of the pattern, and then play them on your bells!

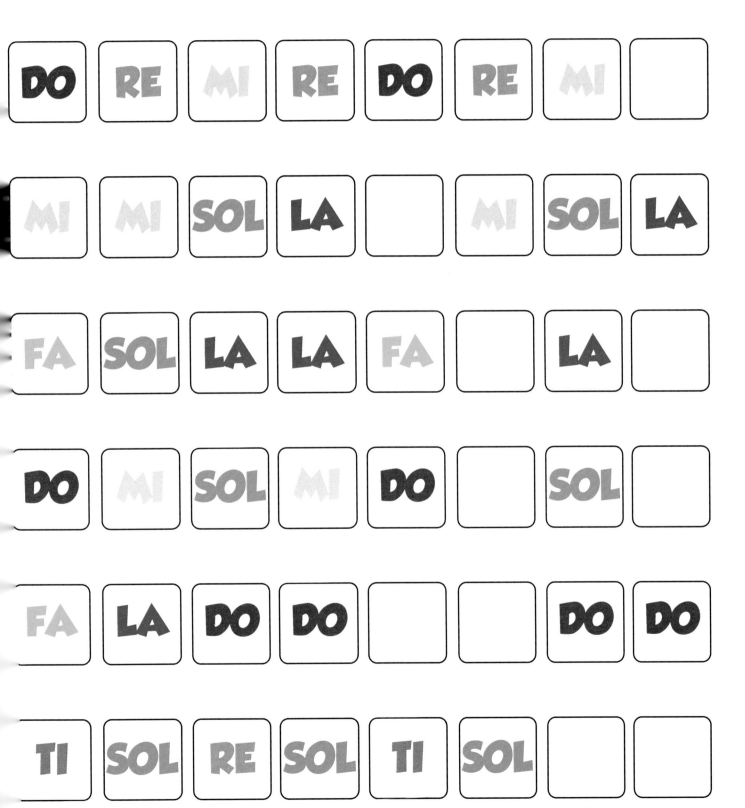

DO	RE	MI	RE	DO	RE	MI	

MI	MI	SOL	LA		MI	SOL	LA

FA	SOL	LA	LA	FA		LA	

DO	MI	SOL	MI	DO		SOL	

FA	LA	DO	DO			DO	DO

TI	SOL	RE	SOL	TI	SOL		

Write a Song Using
DO RE MI FA SOL LA TI DO

Write a song using the numbers above, and then play it on your bells!

_____ Title _____ | _____ Composer _____

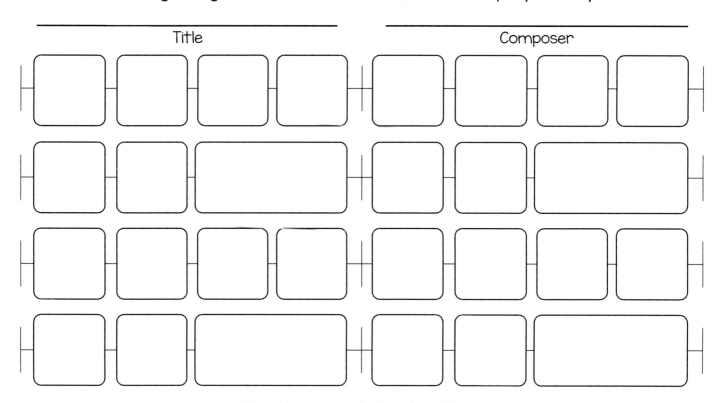

Use the space below to either
1. Write another melody
2. Write lyrics (words) for the melody above

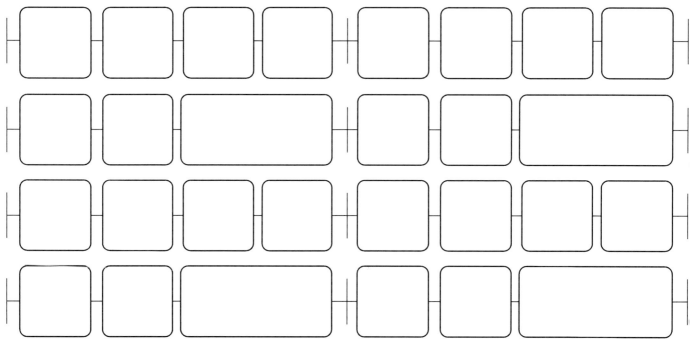

Chapter 8 ♪ Section 6: Twinkle Twinkle Little Star ♪ Lesson Guide

Objective
By the end of this section, students should be able to play "Twinkle Twinkle Little Star".

Overview
In this section, students play "Twinkle Twinkle Little Star", and learn a few facts about Mozart.

Essential Question
How can a student play "Twinkle Twinkle Little Star"?

Instruction Tips
If students struggle to correctly identify steps and skips, try building physical steps out of books or stairs. Then have students place their bells on top of each tier and play them that way.

Materials
- Full Set of C Major Deskbells
- Full Set of Crayons
- Twinkle Twinkle Little Star Video Access
- Workbook pages: 80-85

Table of Contents

Complementary Activities
Ask students how they remembered which notes when where in the Note Stars activity. Do they have any tricks that help them remember where each note lives.

Section 8.6 Video Annotations

0:00 Explain to students that in this video they will be playing the famous song "Twinkle Twinkle Little Star" using C, D, E, F, & A.

1:50 Mr. Rob sings the Solfège names instead of the lyrics to "Twinkle Twinkle Little Star".

3:05 Mr. Rob sings the scale degrees instead of the Solfège names.

Twinkle Twinkle Little Star

Lesson 8.6

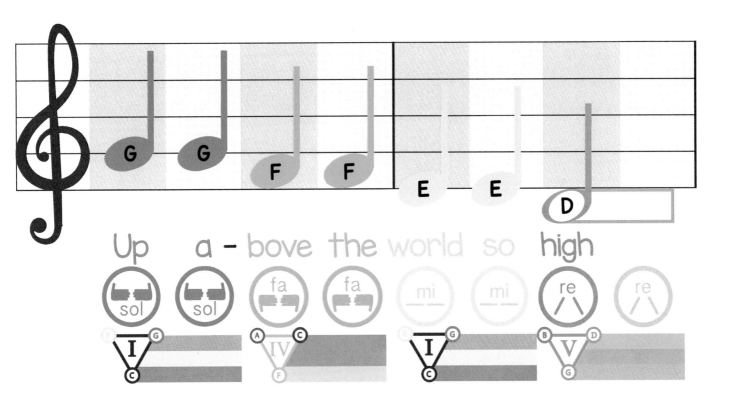

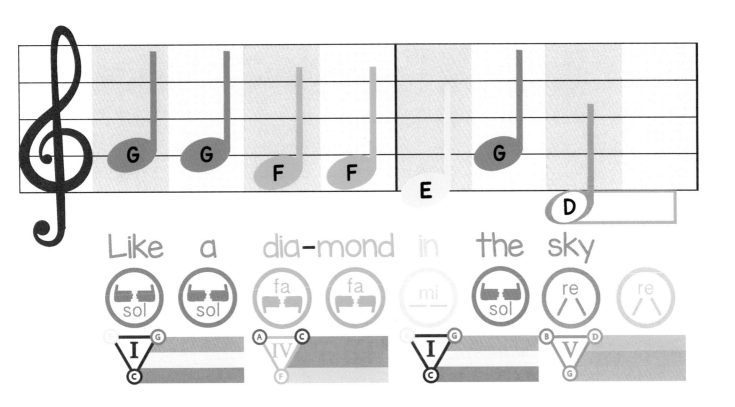

REPEAT 1st PAGE - THEN END !

Mozart

The composer of this song is named Wolfgang Amadeus Mozart. Mozart is a world-famous prodigy who was writing and performing music at age 5! He played the keyboard and violin and wrote over 600 pieces of music, including the melody that we use for "Twinkle Twinkle Little Star," "Baa Baa Black Sheep" and "The ABCs."

Twinkle Little Star

Wolfgang Amadeus

Mozart

Prodigy

Melody

Violin

Piano

Twinkle Twinkle, Steps & Skips

Twinkle Twinkle Little Star uses many steps and a few skips.
Can you draw the correct arrow to indicate steps or skips?

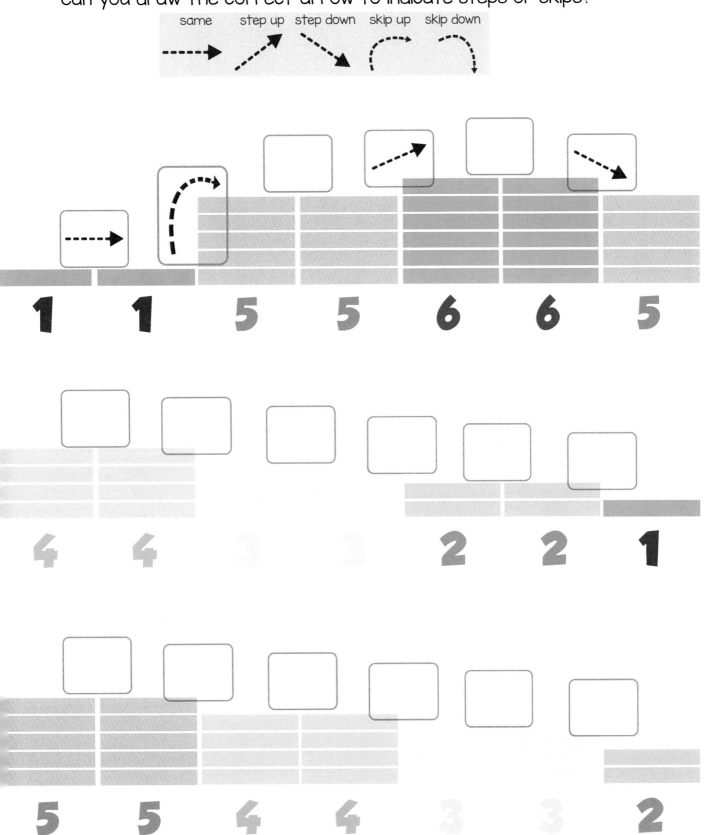

same   step up   step down   skip up   skip down

Note Stars

Some of the letters are missing. Can you fill them in?
Use the letter names that are there to help!
After you fill in the letters, color the stars AND circle any pairs of notes!
Make sure the colors match the bell colors!

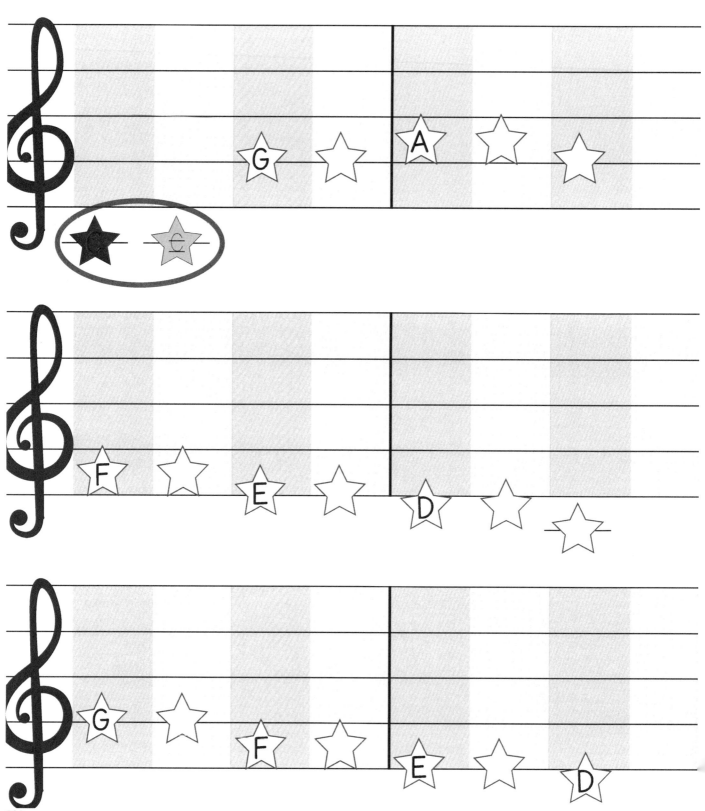

Preschool Prodigies – Chapter Eight Workbook

Finish the Pattern

Finish each line of the pattern using I, IV and V.

I IV V

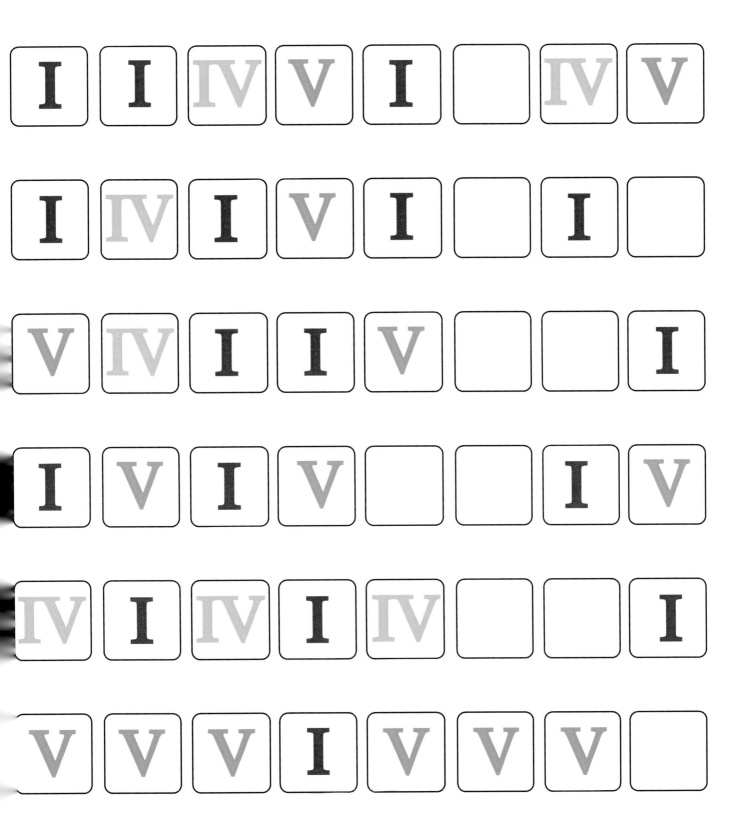

Chapter 8 🎵 Section L: What Note Is It? 🎵 Lesson Guide

Objective

By the end of this section, students should be able to differentiate between G, A & B.

Overview

This section is a listening game. Students will guess between the notes: G, A and B.

Essential Question

How can a student differentiate between the notes: G, A and B?

Instruction Tips

If your students want to play this listening game several times, instead of having them fill out the worksheet, tell them to hold up their G bell, A bell or B bell to indicate their guess.

Materials

- Teal Crayon • Purple Crayon • Pink Crayon
- What Note Is It? Video Access
- Workbook pages: 87

Table of Contents

Complementary Activities

Make up your own listening game with the G, A and B. You could even add in a call and response element by adding patterns.

Section 8.L Video Annotations

0:45 Pause and let your learner guess the first note name before Rex reveals it!

1:10 Pause and let your learner guess the second note name before Rex reveals it!

1:35 Pause and let your learner guess the third note name before Rex reveals it! Explain to students that this will be the last time you pause before moving on. Be sure that your learner is circling his or her guesses on the What Note Is It workbook page.

What Note Is It?

Draw a circle around the bell you hear in each box!

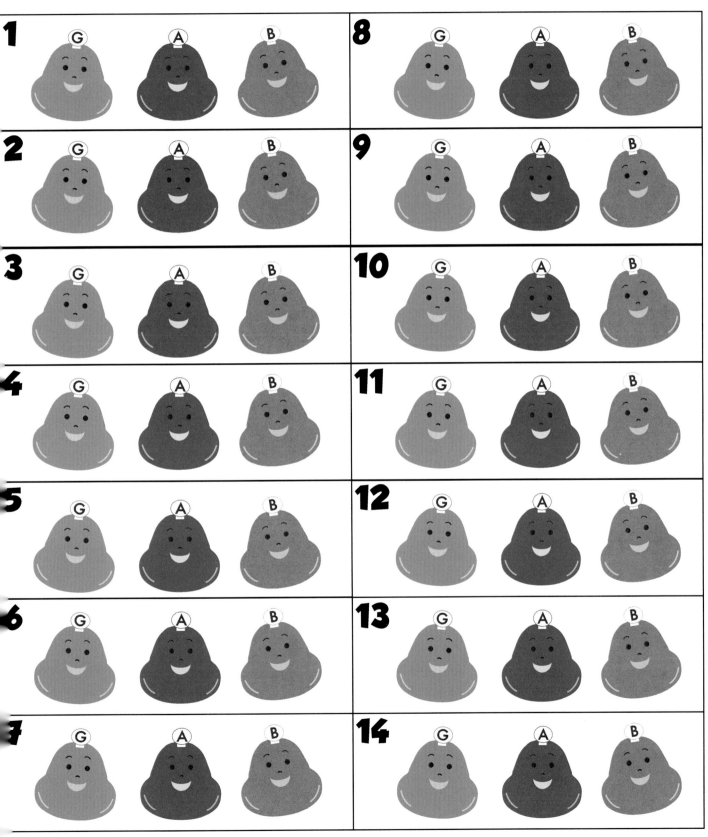

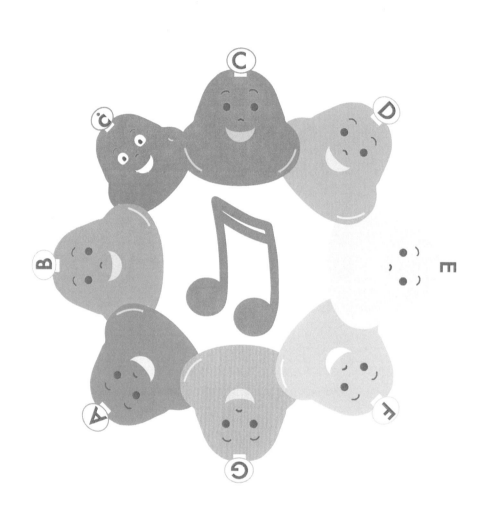

Prodigies Playground
CONGRATULATIONS

You've Completed

Preschool Prodigies

CHAPTER 8

Nice work!

Date

Teacher Signature

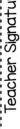

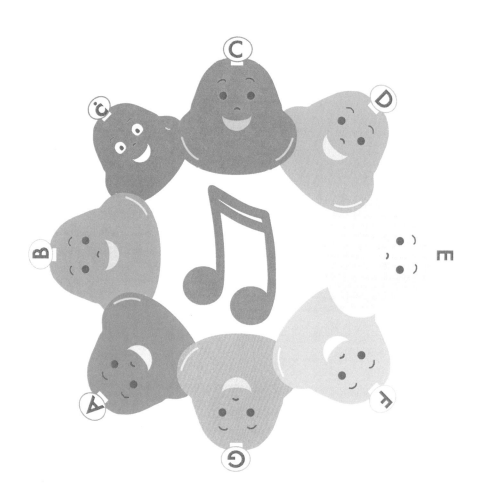

THE RHYTHM TREE

Dear families & teachers,

Welcome to The Rhythm Tree, a bonus rhythm section that takes a slightly different approach than Sweet Beets and Snow Day. The lessons here are a bit less song-oriented and they focus more on a more regimented look at the different note lengths. We'll move away from fruits and vegetables and instead start by using the Kodaly syllables (Ta,Ti Ti, Tika Tika).

Toward the end, we'll move on to counting the rhythms using "1 + 2 + 3 + 4 +" which is the way that musicians normally talk about rhythm.

The sheet music in this series mimics some popular rhythm methods in it's approach. Likewise, the printables in this book mimic popular classroom materials. This section is a simple, colorful and kid-friendly approach to teaching methods that have been around for a long time.

Don't forget that really mastering these pages takes a lot of repetition. Ideally, your learners will be able to perform the following pages, without the video, and with a metronome. The call-and-response format of the videos is easy to follow, but the timing, coordination and steady beat required to play the pages is going to take some regular practice.

I used many of these exact patterns for years and years of practice by simply playing these pages on different parts and/or with different limbs of the drumset. My method book had years worth of dates, check marks, notes, beat up pages and crazy ideas, and hopefully yours will, too!

Practice often, and make sure to use the cut-outs for some rhythmic arranging of your own. You can even combine these cut-outs with some of the pitch-based cut-outs to write some more rhythm specific music!

Happy Musicing!

– Mr. Rob & the Prodigies Team

Lesson 1 - Whole and Half Notes

Clap, tap or drum your way through each line TWICE before moving onto the next

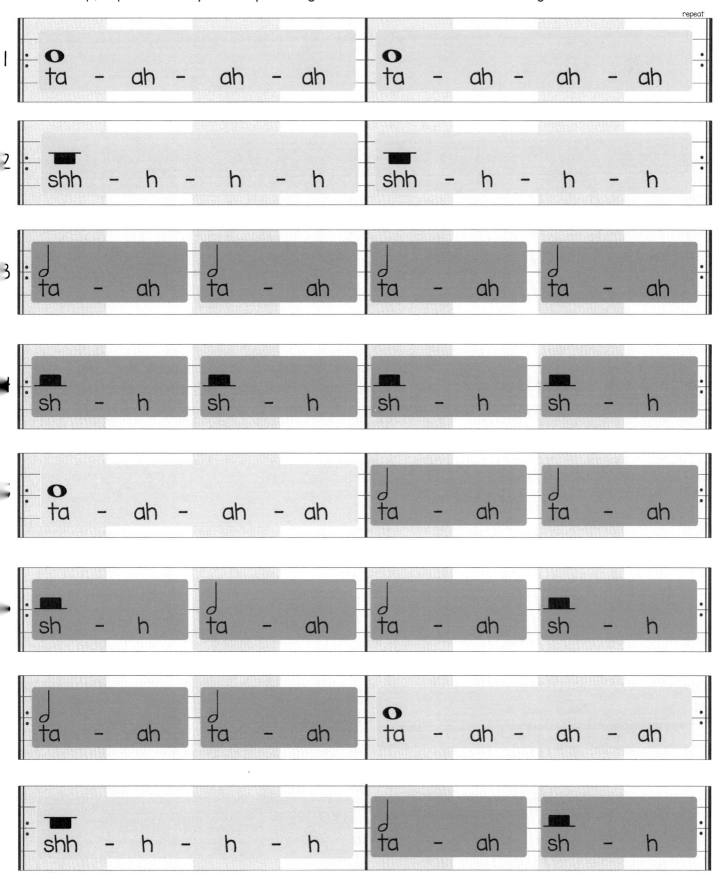

Lesson 2 – Half and Quarter Notes

Clap, tap or drum your way through each line TWICE before moving onto the next line!

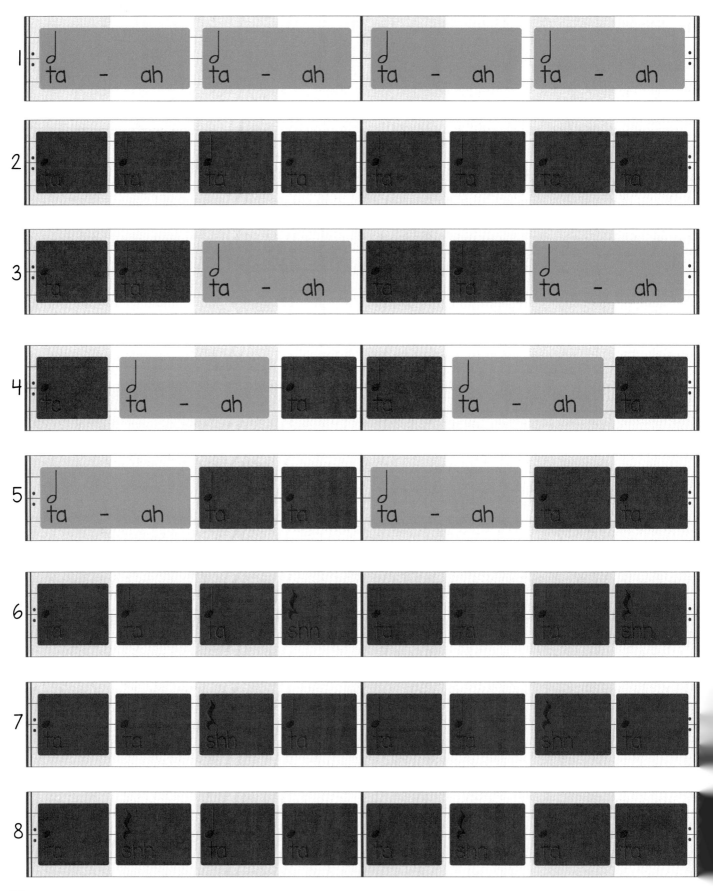

Clap, tap or drum your way through each line TWICE before moving onto the next line!

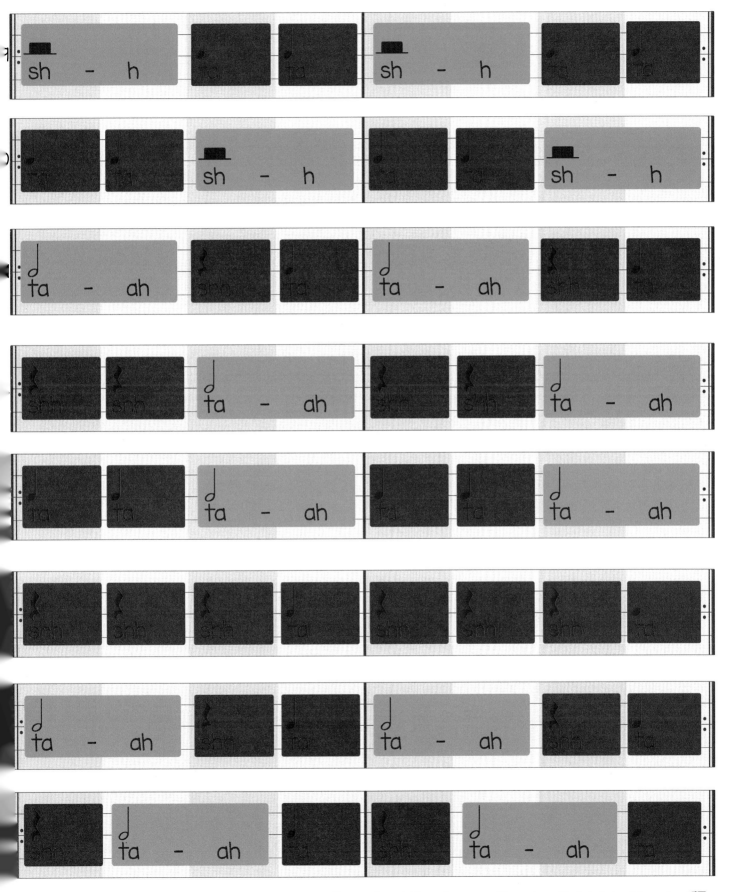

Lesson 3 – Quarter Notes and Eighth Note

Clap, tap or drum your way through each line TWICE before moving onto the next line!

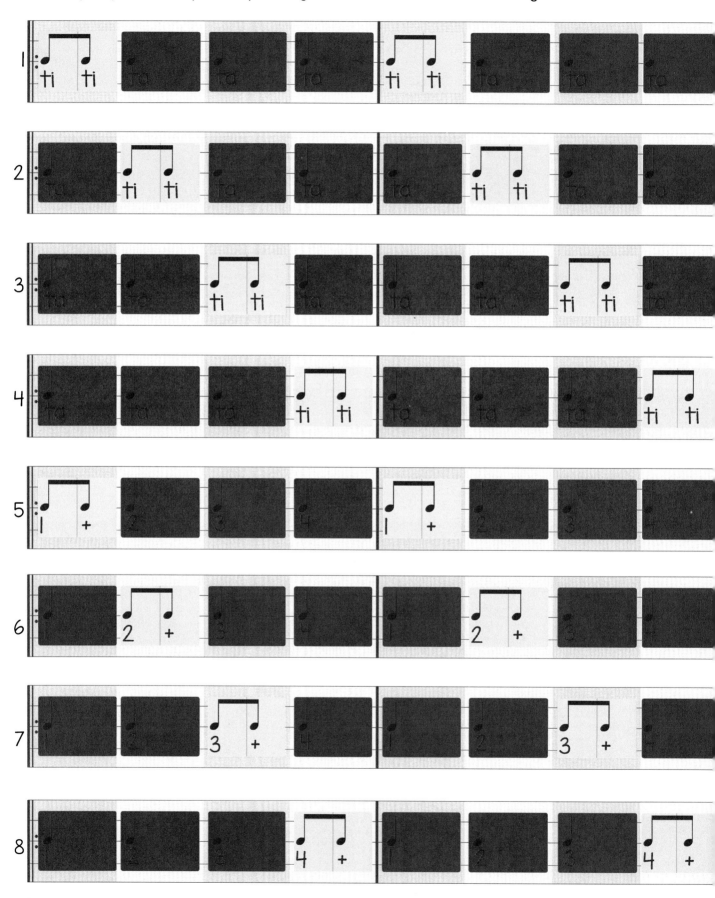

Once you can play these patterns with your hands, try stomping a steady Ta with one foot and then play these rhythms on top of the steady Ta.

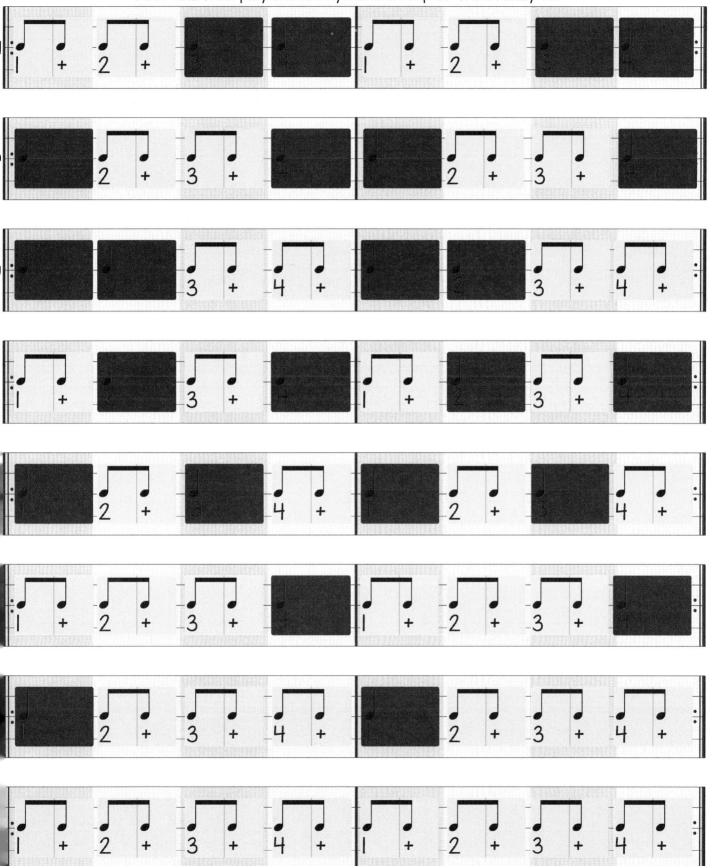

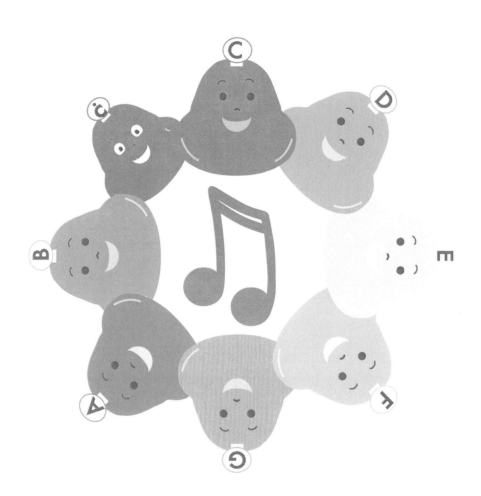

Rhythm Tree Cut-Outs

Cut out the notes below and use them to make patterns of your very own! Make sure to use both of your hands when you're playing faster rhythms!

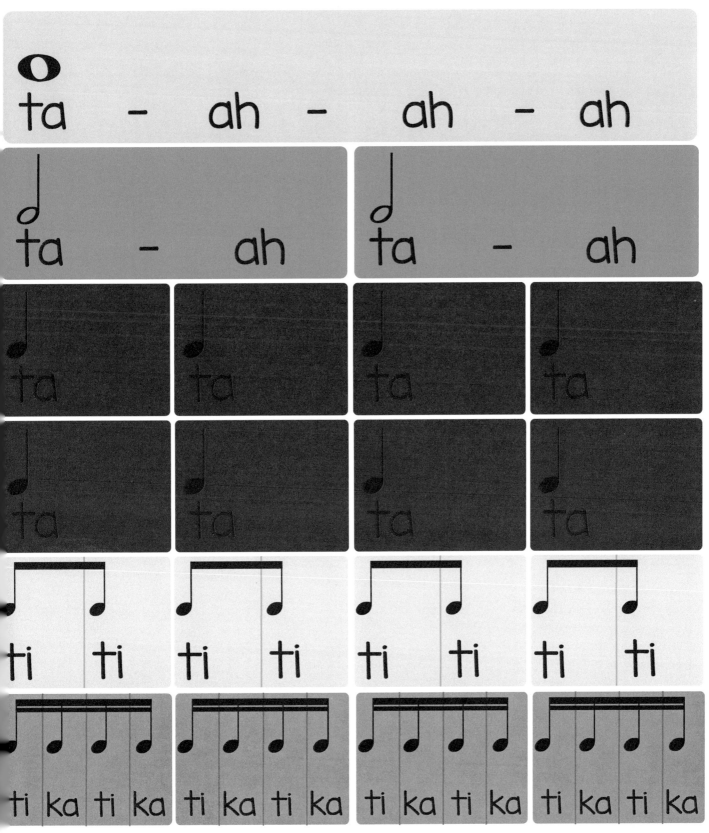

Rhythm Tree Cut-Outs

Cut out the notes below and use them to make patterns of your very own! Make sure to use both of your hands when you're playing faster rhythms!

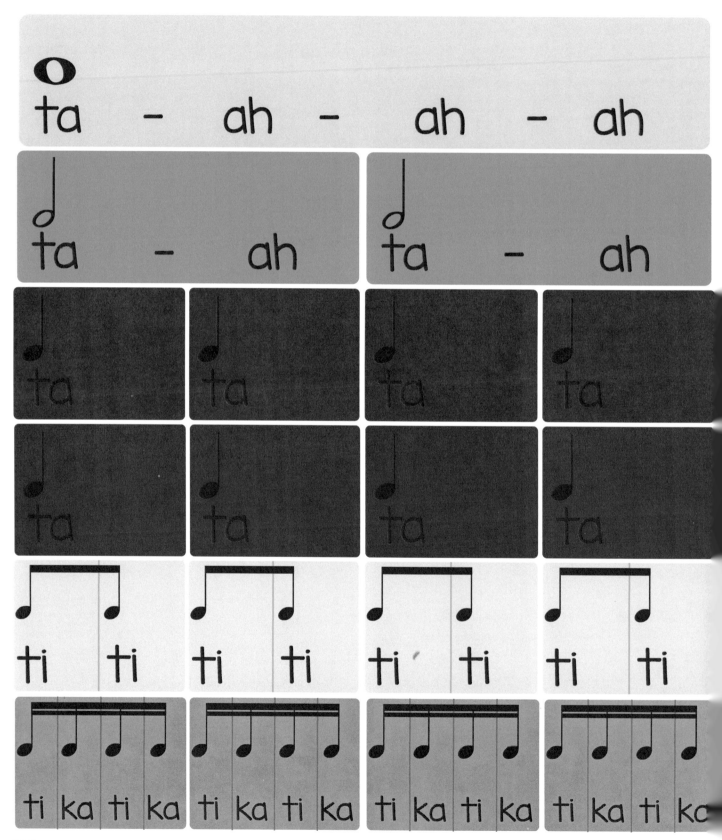

Rest Cut-Outs

Below are the rests! You can use these to mix up your musical play as well.

shh — h — h — h

shh — h

shh — h

shh

shh

shh

shh

shh

shh

shh

shh

shh	shh	shh	shh	shh	shh	shh	shh
shh	+	shh	+	shh	+	shh	+

Rest Cut-Outs

Below are the rests! You can use these to mix up your musical play as well.

shh   -   h   -   h   -   h

shh   -   h

shh   -   h

shh   shh   shh   shh

shh   shh   shh   shh

shh	shh	shh	shh	shh	shh	shh	shh
shh	+	shh	+	shh	+	shh	+

Note Cut-Outs

These cards will help your learners familiarize themselves with the rhythm vocabulary.

Note Cut-Outs
These cards will help your learners familiarize themselves with the rhythm vocabulary.

52944232R00060

Made in the USA
Columbia, SC
08 March 2019